# THE COLLECTED PRINTS OF

# *Ben Shahn*

The Catalogue by Kneeland McNulty

An Essay & Commentary by the Artist

PHILADELPHIA MUSEUM OF ART

*Philadelphia, Pennsylvania · 1967*

# The Collected Prints of Ben Shahn

*With a partial list of his books and posters, published in conjunction with an exhibition of Ben Shahn's Graphics, held at the Philadelphia Museum of Art, November 15 — December 31, 1967.*

*Photograph of Ben Shahn by Yousuf Karsh, 1966*

# Foreword

Ben Shahn epitomizes the liberal American of the thirties and forties whose concern for the well-being of his country and the rights of the individual dominates his life and thought. He cares for humanity with a passion. Curiously enough, no other American artist of our times has allowed his social-political concerns to dominate his art to the extent that Ben Shahn has. One wonders whether his doing this so intensely is a reflection of his Russian origin. In any case, whether the subject is an overtly political matter or a more broadly general statement of the human experience, this artist handles it with a poignancy made only more forceful by his system of abstraction and simplification. There has probably been no artist quite like him in the history of western art although, admittedly, such unbridled feeling for the simple man could only have happened in our time.

As tends to be the case generally of the artist who is as distinguished in graphics as he is in painting, Shahn's pictures are far better known than his prints — although the frequency with which in other contexts some of his graphic images have been reproduced, i.e., the war posters, the Phoenix, the television aerials or the orchestra chairs, has assured certain of the uninitiated a greater awareness of his work than of that by most artists. It is difficult to evade the message of his works when they are encountered. His graphic work is absolutely essential if one hopes to achieve the fullest understanding of this distinguished artist. There one finds the casual thoughts and observations which may never be synthesized in a more formal painting but are nonetheless essential to a total understanding of the man; there too he often deals with more specifically immediate issues, i.e., the Goldwater poster, that need not be pursued further to a broader generalization.

This *catalogue raisonné* of Ben Shahn's graphic work to date, prepared by the Philadelphia Museum of Art's Curator of Prints and Drawings, Kneeland McNulty, on the occasion of the Museum's exhibition of this material, is one of a series of such catalogues. Complete checklists have already been made by the Museum's Department of the work of John Sloan and Edward Hopper while a fully illustrated catalogue dealing with John Marin's etchings is already under way.

*Evan H. Turner, Director*

# Acknowledgments

The preparation of this catalogue has been a pleasure, due largely to the gracious cooperation and tolerance of Ben Shahn who permitted numerous visits to his home in Roosevelt, New Jersey. It provided the most pleasant occasion for the author to make the acquaintance of the artist and his wife. All the quotations, with the exception of two as noted, were elicited from this very busy man who answered endless questions and supplied helpful written comments about his prints. These latter are indicated by his initials following the quotation. It is hoped that Mr. Shahn's speech at the International Design Conference in Aspen, 1966, *In Defense of Chaos,* reprinted here with the kind permission of the author and Allen F. Hurlburt, will provide an insight to the mind of the artist.

Without the cooperation of Mrs. Edith Gregor Halpert, Director of The Downtown Gallery, it would have been impossible to compile the information given here. Mrs. Halpert maintains her own "archives of American art" on such an outstanding group of Americans, including Ben Shahn, that her assistance is essential to the success of any written project dealing with these artists. Much of the material in this catalogue is due to her interest and cooperation.

Mr. Yousuf Karsh of Ottawa, world famous portrait photographer, who permitted the use of his portrait of Joan Miró in an earlier catalogue, has most kindly allowed the reproduction of his forceful portrait of Ben Shahn to be used as a frontispiece here.

Mr. Sol Libsohn, photographer and neighbor of Mr. Shahn, has provided some early pictures of the artist in his studio.

The design of this catalogue is the work of Mr. John Anderson of Northland Press, Flagstaff, Arizona, better known to admirers of fine printing as the proprietor of The Pickering Press.

Others who have assisted or encouraged the production of this work are most gratefully acknowledged: Dr. Evan H. Turner, Director of the Philadelphia Museum of Art; Mr. Alfred J. Wyatt, staff photographer; Mrs. Barbara Malinsky of the Department of Prints and Drawings; Miss Virginia Allen; Dr. and Mrs. Harry Bakwin, who lent their *Levana* portfolio for photographing; Harold Hugo; Miss Eva Lee; George Nakashima; and Bernarda B. Shahn.

*Kneeland McNulty*

PHOTOGRAPHY CREDITS:
   *Dr. Harry Bakwin: 25–34*
   *The Downtown Gallery, New York: 9, 10, 15, 18, 21, 23, 39, 39A, 41, 43, 44, 54, 60, 61A, 66, 68A, 73*
   *Eva Lee Gallery, Great Neck, L.I., New York: 22*
   *Lawyers Constitutional Defense Committee, American Civil Liberties Union, New York: 69b, c, d, e*
   *Philadelphia Museum of Art for the remainder.*

# Contents

*Photograph by Sol Libsohn*

*Photograph by Sol Libsohn*

# Ben Shahn as a Printmaker

Printer's ink has always been in Ben Shahn's blood; the urge to print has never deserted him. From early childhood he was trained as a commercial lithographer, and when he left that trade in 1932 he had already taken an ambitious yet frustrating step toward becoming a printmaker. Through the years he has continued to make prints whenever he had the inclination, or whenever he had the time between his other activities as painter, draftsman, and photographer, or designer of stained glass windows, tapestries, and books.

Shahn was born in 1898 in Kovno, Russia ( for a time it was a Lithuanian town ), and emigrated to the United States with his parents in 1906. The family settled in Brooklyn where his father, a cabinetmaker, took up business.

In his book, *Love and Joy about Letters*, Shahn says, "In 1913, when I was fourteen years old, I was apprenticed to a lithographer. By this time I had finished elementary school and, it was generally agreed, knew everything there was to be known . . . I was apprenticed to a lithographer, and if learning a craft was my ostensible reason and purpose, my private one was to learn to draw — and to draw always better and better.

"But people who drew were the aristocrats of the lithographic trade. First I had to learn the hard things, like grinding stones and running errands and making letters — thousands and thousands of letters until I should know to perfection every curve, every serif, every thick element of a letter and every thin one . . ."

This training was at Hessenberg's, 101 Beekman Street, downtown

New York, where the printing industry flourished. Shahn worked as an apprentice for four years starting at a beginner's pay of one dollar a week, gradually ascending the economic ladder until his weekly earnings were twenty-five times that. His first two years as an apprentice were strictly devoted to the mechanics of the trade: he would spend whole days doing nothing but drawing pages of letters. Not only did he need a proficient and precise forward hand, but he had to acquire the ability to draw everything backwards on a lithograph stone so that his lettering would reverse itself onto the printed sheet. When he produced one or two particularly well-done sheets and showed them to his employer, his highest praise was "that's not bad."

After two years of such diligence, he was allowed to participate more fully in shop productions. His ability to draw helped his career professionally and financially; and he was later on accorded the position of "first light," that is, the position closest to the window. He broke away from his first employer when the discrepancy between the union scale of forty-five dollars per week and his own salary of twenty-five made it apparent that his talents would be better rewarded elsewhere. After that, he worked for a number of different printers and managed a good deal of free lancing.

For those who are familiar with lithography as practiced by artists today, it might come as a surprise to read in Shahn's *Love and Joy about Letters* that, "As a lithographic engraver, I had to learn to work in a precise way, literally to cut the lines I made, working always against the resistant material of the stone . . ." What Shahn was actually doing was incising his drawing into the stone, and not, as is done nowadays, merely drawing on the surface as one draws on a piece of paper. Commercial lithographers, at that time, were competing with other printing industries to produce the effect of engraving and letterpress by the cheaper lithographic medium. A very fine and precise line can be made in a lithograph by scratching the lines into the stone through a hard ground or protective coating. The stone is then prepared for printing, and the result can be a deceptive facsimile of almost any other graphic technique. Thus a lithograph can duplicate nearly any printing medium. It can produce this effect more economically, particularly if a large edition is required, for multiple impressions can be made at one time by repeatedly transferring the image from a small stone onto a larger one. Thus thirty exactly similar images can be printed at one time. To produce duplicate impressions from a copper engraving requires inking and printing each time.

Unfortunately Shahn has not preserved any examples of his work from this period. Presumably the products from his own hand would be indistinguishable from those of the other craftsmen, lost in the anonymity of "shop" work.

As his technical skill developed, and along with it a strong desire to be an artist, Shahn was gradually able to support himself by taking a few well-paid commissions of a commercial nature. These earned him sufficient money to support him through the difficult period when he was breaking away from his early training, with its guaranteed livelihood, to the more challenging and rewarding profession of artist. Shahn mentions one instance of this sort when he was offered two hundred dollars to produce a poster. Due to his technical skill and knowledge of the business, he accomplished this in a day. His client objected to paying that amount for only one day's work, but reluctantly did so. By living frugally, Shahn was then financially free to do as he pleased for several months, devoting his time to his painting, drawing, and traveling.

His final break with commercial lithography came during the Depression. Shahn had been out of the country — he made trips to Europe and North Africa in 1925, 1927 and 1929 (see his *Algerian Memory* (no. 1) based on a drawing from an old sketchbook made in Djerba, Tunis in 1929) — and sometime after his return asked for work in the lithographic industry. Jobs, however, were scarce; industry had suffered from competition from more modern printing methods. The union told him that while he had been away his colleagues had had a difficult time maintaining their status and the union would not jeopardize one of them for what they considered to be Shahn's opportunism.

Meanwhile Shahn had attended New York University and City College of New York from 1919 to 1922. He accepted a summer scholarship in biology at Woods Hole in 1921 because, as he admits, he wanted to draw fish. In 1922 he left City College for courses at the National Academy of Design.

When he came back from Europe in 1929 he began to look for a gallery. He exhibited a few times in the annual Christmas show at the Whitney Club; and in 1930 he was given his first one-man exhibit at The Downtown Gallery by its Director and still present owner, Mrs. Edith Gregor Halpert. He has maintained his allegiance to that gallery ever since.

His importance as a painter was firmly established by the exhibition at The Downtown Gallery in 1932 of twenty-three gouaches based on the trial of Sacco and Vanzetti (see *Passion of Sacco and Vanzetti*, no. 42). From then on he received intermittent commissions which did not fully meet his financial needs, and in 1935 he joined the W. P. A., taking jobs off and on with federal agencies as his financial situation required. "I became a bureaucrat," he says. Among the agencies which utilized his talents were the Federal Emergency Relief Administration, the Resettlement Administration, and the Farm Security Administration.

Despite the fact that Shahn had come to detest the smell of lithographic tusche, his first prints were in this medium. In 1931 he produced a portfolio of ten lithographed illustrations to Thomas De Quincey's *Levana and Our Ladies of Sorrow* (nos. 25-34). It sold very poorly, no more than ten copies Shahn believes, and the remainder of the edition he destroyed in anger and frustration. In 1936 he again tried lithography with a single print for the Resettlement Administration, *Seward Park* ( no. 54 ); and then abandoned that medium, with the exception of poster work, until 1963, when he worked in Paris at the lithograph shop of Fernand Mourlot. There he produced, in conjunction with the master printer A. Manaranche, a group of prints closely related to his serigraphs: *Blind Botanist* ( no. 8 ); *Mask* ( no. 38 ); and *Psalm 133* ( no. 52 ). He has most recently worked with Gemini, G.E.L. in Los Angeles ( no. 24 ).

During 1940-1942 Shahn and his wife, Bernarda Bryson, were commissioned by the Section of Fine Arts, Public Buildings Administration, U. S. Treasury to execute some large murals in egg tempera for the Social Security Building, Washington, D. C. There was some difficulty with the plaster, and while a new coat was drying they returned to their home in Roosevelt, New Jersey, where they continue to live. Shahn decided he would learn to silkscreen. This despite the fact that he had met the art dealer, J. B. Neumann, who, Shahn says, could not share his enthusiasm for Gauguin because Gauguin made "prints." At any rate, Shahn had become acquainted with a number of artists in the W. P. A., such as Hyman Warsager and Anthony Velonis, who showed him how to prepare silk screens and print from them.

His first silk screen trial print was *Immigrant Family*, 1941 ( no. 23 ), followed by other subjects which reflected his painting style: *Prenatal Clinic* ( no. 49 ); *4 1/2 Out of Every 5* ( no. 18 ); *Vandenberg, Dewey, and Taft* ( no. 60 ); and *The Handshake* ( no. 21 ).

Some of his early serigraphs were distributed as Christmas cards: *Deserted Fair Ground* ( no. 16 ) was one of these, as was *Boy on a Tricycle* ( no. 9 ). It was Shahn's hope that these prints, sent to all his friends, would atone for his being such a poor correspondent, a trait which he and they agree is still characteristic.

It was not until about 1950, when he made *Silent Music* ( no. 55 ), that he produced a serigraph in a *consciously* limited edition.

Just previous to this he had made about three hundred impressions of *Where There Is a Book There Is No Sword* ( no. 63 ) which had also been given away as Christmas cards. One of these he discovered hanging on a nail in the basement of a friend's house. Determined to stop such desecration, he returned home to number the 145 remaining prints in the edition, hoping that this would impart to them some kind of inviolability.

*Where There Is a Book There Is No Sword* and *Silent Music* anticipated Shahn's new print style: the simple statement made with a slightly jagged single line. With this distinctive line Shahn has lead a host of imitators in the fine and commercial art fields.

Over the next few years, Shahn produced those prints for which he is best known: *Triple Dip* (no. 58), *Phoenix* (no. 45), *TV Antennae* (no. 59), *Paterson* (nos. 43, 44), *Lute and Molecule* (no. 35), *Alphabet of Creation* (no. 3), *Supermarket* (no. 57), *Wheat Field* (no. 62), and *Passion of Sacco and Vanzetti* (no. 42).

*Triple Dip* (no. 58), which was drawn directly on the screen as opposed to tracing a drawing, was inspired by a daily ritual performed while his children were theoretically quarantined for chicken pox. Each day, when the children were well enough, their father would take them through the woods and away from human contact, to the store where he would buy them ice-cream cones.

Of prints such as *Supermarket, Silent Music, TV Antennae* and *Wheat Field*, Shahn says they "are among the abiding symbols of American daily life, to be celebrated and brought into awareness."

Shahn has repeatedly expressed his concern for the image making function of the artist. In regard to his own work, he mentions four recurrent themes: *people who wait*-endlessly, and when whatever it is arrives, they wait again, pathetic people such as those in *Prenatal Clinic* (no. 49); *scientism*, where pure research can turn against the researcher, as in the *Blind Botanist* (no. 7) who is unwittingly punctured and torn by the material he studies; *aloneness*, the sense of vacuity given in *Deserted Fair Ground* (no. 16), or *Silent Music* (no. 55); and *indestructability of the spirit of man* which is defiantly apparent in *I Think Continually of Those Who Were Truly Great* (no. 22), and *Passion of Sacco and Vanzetti* (no. 42).

*Alphabet of Creation*, 1957 (no. 3) represents one of Shahn's delights with lettering and his particular pleasure in the elegance of Hebrew script. *Alphabet* contains the twenty-two letters of the Hebrew alphabet arranged according to Shahn. Shahn first made this design for his book, *The Alphabet of Creation*, and later had a chop, or seal, of it made to stamp his prints. "There is more legendry around the Hebrew alphabet than around probably any other; it has intrigued me since early childhood and has continually invaded every other interest and image I've worked with."

Shahn's reiterrated concern with certain themes is apparent in such prints as his *Phoenix* (no. 45), which relates to his "fire paintings," and in his *Passion of Sacco and Vanzetti*, 1958 (no. 42). Twenty-six years earlier, he had painted his famous series of gouaches on this latter subject, and now in 1958 he returned to produce another statement in print. The stark portraits of Nicola Sacco and Bartolomeo Vanzetti are juxtaposed with the simple yet powerful words of Vanzetti, which begin with: "If it had not been for these thing, I might have live out my life talking at street corners to scorning men . . ." Shahn used his silk screen to provide three variations of the one subject: a portrait of the two men, a print of the words alone, and a combination of the words and portraits to make the *Passion*.

Shahn has experimented in a number of ways with his silk screen prints. In the color version of *Phoenix* ( no. 45 ), for instance, Shahn painted in the colors first, and then printed the black image. He felt that this would provide a richness of color that could not be obtained by simply printing the colors; he did not follow the usual procedure of printing the black as a key-plate and then filling that with color. He followed the same process in *Mine Building* ( no. 41 ) and *Triple Dip* ( no. 58 ).

*I Think Continually of Those Who Were Truly Great* ( no. 22 ) is another example of an unusual practice. Very little of that picture is actually printed: the letters were silk-screened, and the beak of the dove was made by stamping with the tip of an art gum eraser. The remainder of each print is created by a wash of hand-applied, gray watercolor outlining the body of the dove. A comparison of any two impressions of this print will show that the shape of the dove varies slightly because each has been made by hand.

In *Alphabet and Warsaw* ( no. 61A ) and *Alphabet and Maximus* ( no. 39A ), both unique prints which are called "silk screen and rubbing," Shahn cut a piece of cardboard into the shape of *Alphabet of Creation* ( no. 3 ) and made a rubbing of this onto an extra proof of *Warsaw* ( no. 61 ) and of *Maximus of Tyre* ( no. 39 ).

Lately Shahn has been experimenting with the effect that can be achieved when a silk screen is partially cleaned with solvent: a very rough line results. An example of this is shown in the contrast between two impressions of *Ecclesiastes* ( no. 17, 17A ), one printed normally, and the other printed after the screen was partially cleaned. Shahn feels that he will eventually be able to control this effect.

---

Shahn's attitude about prints shows a perversity toward dogma and conformity. To the purist who demands that each print in an edition be an exact duplicate of every other print in that edition, he deserves no place and receives no honor. He has broken almost every rule in the books. To some his most heinous crime is his application of color by hand, which immediately makes each print differ from its companion. To others his most grievous fault is not to number his editions. Others will complain that they cannot distinguish his "original prints" from mechanical reproductions of his drawings; or they will object to the fact that he signs both original prints and reproductions, thus further confusing the issue. Others are unable to grasp the difference between work by the artist's own hand, and those designs which have been duplicated by Leonard Baskin, Stefan Martin, or A. Manaranche.

Shahn has no intention of dissembling. He merely has his own ideas about the purpose of an image. When Shahn has an idea for a picture he develops as many drawings for it as his imagination allows. Many of the drawings will be very similar, a little change here or a little change there; or they may develop into an entirely new subject. As he says, "working drawings can open up new interests." These drawings may be used immediately, or at some later date, and may develop into paintings, gouaches, finished drawings, prints, book illustrations, posters, stained-glass windows, or even tapestry. There is nothing sacred about their purpose, and the artist feels that he may use them as freely as he wishes, repeating them in various media; because the image is more important than the medium.

Shahn considers printmaking primarily a means to proliferate drawings. This is in contrast to some printmakers who consciously utilize the peculiar qualities of each print medium to achieve a particular effect. To show that Shahn has not attempted to exploit the unique qualities of silk screen printing one need only to look through a few catalogues where his serigraphs have been mislabeled "lithographs."

It is readily understandable why Shahn, trained in the lithographic profession, displays a lack of concern for the concept of the multiple original print. Shahn's own definition of an original print is one that is made without the intervention of photography. An original work of art should be totally one person's work, he feels. Since it is really the image that counts, he is not so concerned with the philosophy of original versus non-original as are many theorists. He does not consider original, for instance, those zinc lithographs which he made at Mourlot's in Paris. He worked there so closely with the printer that he added to each plate the inscription: "A. MANARANCHE, Grav. LITH." Mourlot's is one of the most efficient lithograph workshops in the world. As a printer and graphic designer, Shahn enjoyed the advantages of working with a master printer whose ability Shahn could not match. With infinite skill, such a printer can produce the most subtle tones, and most delicate lines. Sometimes Manaranche would even draw on the plate along with Shahn.

So far as hand coloring his prints is concerned, Shahn could cite precedents that would negate any argument against that practice. From the fifteenth century on, prints have been colored by hand; and generally those that have been colored by a contemporary hand bring more at the marketplace than black-and-white versions. It is only in very recent times that the concept of exact duplication of every print in an edition has been considered correct and proper.

Shahn has even enlisted the help of his family in applying color to his prints: his son Jonathan, and his daughter Suzie, helped to color *Supermarket, Mine Building,* and *Pleiades. Phoenix* ( no. 45 ) was entirely colored by Shahn himself. A number of Shahn's prints appear both colored and uncolored. Shahn finds the actual process of hand

7

coloring tedious and often will not actually apply the color until he has an order. Even more difficult and time consuming is the application of gold leaf by hand on such prints as *Decalogue* ( no. 15 ) or *Menorah* ( no. 40 ) or *Pleiades* ( no. 46 ). The term "theorem" was applied to these hand-colored prints by Mrs. Halpert who was familiar with the 19th century technique of "theorem" or "Poonah painting" which referred to beautifully stencilled pictures on velvet.

Shahn stopped numbering his editions after realizing the futility of trying to guess the edition size of one of the most famous prints in the world, Antonio Pollaiuolo's *Battle of the Naked Man*, ca. 1470, which he saw when it was offered for purchase to a museum director friend. There are only fifty or so known impressions of this unsigned, unnumbered print, and yet its price is astronomical. It is entirely possible, Shahn reasoned, that a cache of these prints may some day turn up and completely upset their market value. Furthermore, who can ever know the edition size of the engravings of Durer, or etchings by Rembrandt? The whole concept of numbering an edition seemed to Shahn to be a modern affectation.

There are a number of factors, Shahn points out, which naturally limit his editions. He cites, for example, that he may run out of printing ink, or he may run out of paper. Then there is some spoilage likely when color is used. He points out, furthermore, that silk screens deteriorate so that they cannot be saved forever for repeated runs; and, since he often cleans and reuses a screen for another subject, the first image is obliterated. In any case, he does not have room to store all the screens necessary to keep every print available for reprinting. The fact is that he aims for an edition of about one hundred prints. He does not have the inclination to print more, and he certainly lacks the ambition to hand color more than that.

There exists some confusion about the reproductions of Ben Shahn's works which are mistaken for originals ( see nos. 67-71 ). As one cannot help but be aware, Shahn has supported a number of causes by contributing his artistic ability. Sometimes this help will be in the form of a drawing which Shahn will allow to be reproduced in quantity and sold to raise money. The monetary value of such reproductions is often at variance with accepted art market value, just as pictures sold to raise money at a church rally will reflect the generosity of the purchaser and will have little to do with intrinsic value. The fact that Shahn has signed some of these reproductions increases confusion amongst collectors, but it also increases the pictures' value at time of sale. Shahn holds all of these prints in high regard, and he is not concerned with the problem of the uninformed collector; that is a matter that will only be resolved in time, hopefully with the help of documentation such as the present catalogue.

For those who are puzzled by the wood-engravings of Leonard Baskin (nos. 6, 64) and Stefan Martin (nos. 19, 36) after Ben Shahn's drawings, it should be pointed out that time has honored the tradition of reproductive prints throughout the history of printmaking. A traditionalist would immediately recognize a practice that has existed throughout four centuries. All those prints of Michelangelo's or Raphael's work were by other artists, trained as printmakers; while Rubens and Van Dyck employed engravers to duplicate their drawings and paintings. It is an interesting phenomenon to have this tradition repeated in the twentieth century where we are given an opportunity to see two important artists collaborating on one design.

Shahn explains the collaboration in this way. As a member of the jury of the International Graphic Arts Society, which publishes prints that have been approved by the jury, he felt it would be unethical for him to be both juror and printmaker — to receive the financial benefits of a self-granted commission. Therefore, when asked to make prints for I.G.A.S., the obvious solution was to engage the services of his friends Leonard Baskin or Stefan Martin, both of whom enjoy Shahn's admiration and respect.

---

Shahn makes his prints in a studio situated directly behind his home in Roosevelt, New Jersey. In one room of the studio are his silk screen printing frames, and all the equipment he needs to make his prints entirely by hand. He will sometimes draw directly on the screen, but more often, he will prepare a drawing to size and copy it through the transparent mesh of the silk.

He signs his prints variously so that it is difficult to specify any consistent manner. He used to sign with a brush, but discovered that laymen could not distinguish a brush-drawn signature from a printed one. He had become accustomed to signing with a brush when he was working on grained zinc plates which would wear away his pen point, requiring constant re-sharpening. He is now more likely to use a pencil or conté crayon, and since 1960, he has employed the seal, or chop, which is a miniature of his *Alphabet of Creation* (no. 3). While he and his wife were in Japan in 1960, Shahn had the chop made, and purchased a Japanese ink pad with its traditional orange-red color. Although he may apply this seal to an occasional early print that will come his way, its use generally indicates a date following his visit to Japan.

---

In speaking of signing his work, Shahn likes to remark that, if one wants a really rare Shahn book, one should get one that is unsigned. Actually this would not be difficult to do, for Shahn has produced a considerable number of books, many of them still unpublished.

It is only natural that Shahn's involvement with printing and lettering would lead to the production of books. Many of these are intimate documents, little holograph pieces such as illustrated Christmas books for his wife, or an *Alphabet for Tobias* ( Leonard Baskin's son ) or an *Alphabet for Sister Mary Corita.*

Shahn is constantly working on books. Some will be in production stage, as his new *Ecclesiastes,* now being printed in Europe; others are lying on his worktable, their hand-sewn pages open to a blank which will be lettered or decorated as the artist feels the urge. Or one will have just recently appeared in paperback: *The Biography of a Painting,* 1966, for which the original manuscript remains on his bookshelf. It is a remarkable conglomeration of hand lettering, pasted-in prints, original illustrations, and glossy reproductions of paintings which altogether make fascinating reading and looking.

Among his own writing are two delightful books: *The Shape of Content,* 1957, which contains some of the most lucid writing about art that has been written; and his *Love and Joy about Letters,* 1963, from which some quotations have been excerpted above.

One of his favorite books is *Ounce Dice Trice,* 1958, by Alastair Reid, a nonsense book which contains "an odd collection of words and names to amuze and amaze . . ."

Among his more elaborate publications are *Ecclesiastes,* 1965, with several wood-engravings by Stefan Martin after Shahn's drawings; the deluxe edition of *Haggadah for Passover,* 1966, with an original lithographed frontispiece and twelve illustrations elaborately colored by hand-stencils in France, and including several suites of the illustrations on different papers, all in the tradition of the finest French illustrated books; and shortly to be published, another edition of *Ecclesiastes,* hand written and illustrated by Shahn, reproduced by lithography, collotype and hand-stencilling; and including two original lithographs.

A partial list of Shahn's books is appended to this catalogue.

---

Another facet of Shahn's graphic work is his poster art. Because he is more interested in the image than the medium, he considers his posters equal in importance to his other work, although none of his posters is an original in the sense that the artist produced it entirely by hand from beginning to end. Even his *Goldwater* poster ( no. 68 ), which comes closest to resembling an original print, was made from a photographically prepared silk screen.

Shahn's posters seem to divide into two groups: political and pictorial. Political posters include those made for the CIO Political Action Committee, the Committee for Sane Nuclear Policy, the National Citizens Political Action Committee, the U. S. Office of War Information, War Production Drive Headquarters, United Textile Workers of America, and the like; while the pictorial posters advertise art exhibits and

10

concerts. As "a man with a cause," Shahn comes on loud and clear in his political posters, whereas his pictorial subjects have a gaiety and lyrical quality that sets them quite apart; although perhaps his most humorous picture in any medium is his political satire of Goldwater.

---

For many years Shahn has been a dean among American graphic artists. His ability to create images and his skill with lettering have made him one of the most influential and imitated artists of our era. We cannot know how well his work will withstand the test of time, but his philosophy — an all pervading concern for mankind which is manifested from a hard-hitting political poster to a children's book illustrated with loving care, from a print that includes the words of Martin Luther "I have the right to believe freely . . .," to a drawing dedicated to the cause of civil rights — this philosophy must surely endure. We are fortunate that an artist of Ben Shahn's stature has used his talents to focus our attention on these concerns.

*Kneeland McNulty*
Philadelphia, November, 1967

11

# In Defense of Chaos

*Reprinted by permission of The International Design Conference in Aspen, 1966*

As a guest and interloper during the past week of enlightenment, I carry with me a heavy sense of guilt. I have heard and seen my environment being built around me and above my head; I have seen the doors closed and the windows locked. I have faced my diet of plankton; I have seen my linens replaced by paper — all to be well-ordered for me by benign and unseen forces . . . and I have said not one word in defense of Chaos!

I love Chaos; it is the mysterious, unknown road. It is the ever-unexpected, the way out; it is freedom; it is man's only hope. It is the poetic element in a dull and ordered world!

I am sure you think that I'm only amusing myself; well, that too, but I am serious. And I would like to communicate to you some little notion of what I conceive Chaos to be, and why I think that it is our unsung and uncelebrated human friend.

Insofar as I know, Chaos is utterly disallowed by science. The very notion of Chaos runs counter to any acceptable logic. Every object upon which we place our hands is part of some physical order; every object has its evolutionary history and its future existence either of long endurance or of predictable decay. And every part of this process is orderly. Every act of ours and every notion of the mind has also its history of impulses, exposures and connections. And all this is order. The macrocosms and the microcosms obey their proper physical laws. Where, then is Chaos?

13

Even as any order of being — including me as an order and you as an order, unfolds through space and time, absorbs and reflects and digests its environment — as any such order pursues its own way, developing its individual shape and form, so are there other such orders — thousands and millions of them unfolding too, wholly independently of each other. All are ordered within themselves and to their environment. But their courses through space and time may be completely unrelated, each one following and making its own rules. The disorderly element, the unpredictable, unforseeable item is the moment of impact between two such orders. That is pure accident. It is the moment of Chaos. It may also be an act of Chaos. It may be deliberately undertaken by a conscious individual.

In nature, it is out of such conflicts between orders that the great changes have come about, the geologic upheavals, the earthquakes, the continental and celestial disturbances. In life, the mutations in species have probably been due to such conflicts between orders. In the processes of thinking, the great social changes, the revolutions, the overturns of tradition have been brought about by conflicts in order — between orders.

None of these episodes has any innate quality of being good or bad; they may be either beneficial or harmful to man; if they are sufficiently inexplicable we call them "acts of God."

But within the area of man's life and his thinking, there are fierce conflicts of orders, and there is fierce conflict between order and disorder. All such conflicts have what are called "value" aspects. Some prove to have been good; others prove to have been bad, and all claim to be good.

Among the thousand varieties of classification that might be applied to the fierce struggles between order and disorder in the human arena, there is one that I find especially interesting. That is the division — the conflict — between omniscience and/or tyranny on the one hand, and Chaos, or the-breaking-out-to-freedom on the other. I have had to name this breaking-out-to-freedom "Chaos" for the simple reason that a break for freedom is always a disruption of established order.

( I am certainly not condemning order as such; we could not live or breathe for a day without it. But neither can I accept it as an unqualified good. Sometimes we cannot breathe within it! )

However generous it may be in its intention omniscience is a dangerous quality in us. Let us say that a designer has designed a living space so perfect in all its dimensions that no one takes issue with it. It has everything; extreme thoughtfulness and understanding have provided for every one of the dweller's needs. There are the conveniences; there is beauty everywhere; there is equipment for ministration to the sick; food is provided, and entertainment; there is paper for the writer and paint for the painter and aphrodisiacs for the poor in spirit. Noth-

14

ing is wanting. The occupants move around, function smoothly; time glides along.

No one wants to break out of this perfect place; there is no reason to. Through the days and the nights the bolts gradually slide into place along the windows; the locks rust on the doors. All exits, unused as they are, become sealed.

But no one actually notices this condition until the ever-restless poet exclaims, "Let's let a little air into this place! I'm suffocating!"

He is roundly condemned. Isn't the place air-conditioned? Who wants the hot, humid outside air? The poet insists; he begins to wrestle with the doorknobs; he tries all the windows. He is a troublemaker, a dissident element. He picks up a chair and throws it through the window and makes his break for freedom. A few people follow but "The Society" stays inside. Not until he comes back with a bouquet of mountain flowers clutched in his hand do the occupants of the living-space begin to question their condition. (The planner, through an oversight had forgotten to install mountain flowers.)

The people go out; they look around themselves — what a heavenly world! They are refreshed; they think of all sorts of things that they can do in the newly-revealed world. They have broken out of the perfect place; they can grow. The poet dies, of course; he has fulfilled himself. He isn't really much mourned, he was such a chaotic element!

I said somewhere before that Chaos is not, even to my mind, an unqualified good; certainly the poet is not the only deliberately chaotic element among us. So is the criminal; and psychologists, omniscient as they are, have frequently aligned the two elements in our society as being essentially the same individual, sharing the same characteristics of temperament.

But there is a difference so profound as to put them at opposite ends of the social scale of good and evil forces. Each one is, within himself, an order, evolved, pre-determined and self-determining. The criminal strikes society with the impact of an order — an organism — built around and out of cruelty and hatreds. His vision is narrow; he is without compassion. His dreams and images are anti-human. He strikes only against, not in behalf of the other person.

The poet is motivated — I think almost always — by pro-human visions. These may not be acceptable to the society within the closed room; they may not even be particularly good for it — not necessarily at all. But the poet seeks freedom, fresh air; he has to breathe; he cannot stand suffocation — he cannot be shackled either by bad design or by good design, he just cannot be shackled. And, in seeking freedom for himself, he sees in his own act liberation for other people and for his society.

There is a very antique legend; it is the oldest one known, that holds Chaos to be a dragon named Tia-mat. According to this legend a cer-

15

tain god, Marduk, was chosen to destroy the dragon of Chaos. There was an historic battle and Chaos/Tia-mat was vanquished. But, most significantly, she was not actually destroyed. She was chained by Marduk who then proceeded to place the north star in the Zenith, to arrange the heavens, separate the water from the earth and create the planned society under which we have been living ever since.

Tia-mat reappears from time to time — almost anyone can see that — and she is quickly subdued again. But she is the dark genius of the artist and the poet, the musician, the dissenter and about three philosophers in every ten thousand. I don't propose to release Chaos and just turn her loose upon the human race — we still must have banks and plane schedules. But I think it would be nice if we just made a pet of her and let her go free from time to time to get a breath of fresh air and romp around a little among the Planned Society.

*Ben Shahn*

# Catalogue of Prints

*This catalogue is arranged alphabetically by title for those single prints which are of particular interest to collectors. An index is provided to assist in finding variant titles and other works by Shahn for which information might otherwise be difficult to locate. It is hoped that this list is complete to date. Partial lists of books and posters are appended.*

---

*Sizes of prints are given in inches, height preceding width.*

## No. 1 ALGERIAN MEMORY, 1959

Serigraph, printed in brown. Composition 16 1/2 x 11 1/2; sheet 26 1/8 x 20 1/8. Unspecified edition size; signed in pencil.

*"This print was done to demonstrate the process of silk-screen printing. It was based on a drawing from an old sketch book made in Djerba (Tunis) in 1929."* B.S.

No. 2  ALL THAT IS BEAUTIFUL, 1965

Serigraph, printed in black, with hand coloring. Composition 24 3/4 x 38 1/4; sheet 26 1/8 x 38 3/4. Unspecified edition size; signed with conté crayon, and red seal.

Lettered:  *"All that is beautiful.  But for remembrance' sake.  The art of Pheidias."*

*"The pain of seeing the city I grew up in being covered by the new wave of concrete and glass."*  B.S.

No. 3  ALPHABET OF CREATION, 1957
also called ALPHABET

Serigraph, printed in black. Composition 30 1/2 x 22; sheet 40 x 27. Unspecified edition size; signed with conté crayon.

*"First designed as a seal for my book, the* Alphabet of Creation. *There is more legendry around the Hebrew alphabet than around probably any other alphabet. The Hebrew alphabet has intrigued me since early childhood and has continually invaded every other interest and image I've worked with."*   B.S.

This design incorporates the 22 letters of the Hebrew alphabet, arranged according to Shahn.

Ben Shahn

### No. 4 AND MINE EYES A FOUNTAIN OF TEARS, 1965

There are two versions of this subject; serigraph, printed in red, with Hebrew lettering, composition 11 3/4 x 10 1/4; sheet 24 1/8 x 18; and serigraph, printed in black, English lettering, composition 11 3/4 x 10 1/4; sheet 18 1/2 x 16 1/8. Unspecified edition sizes; signed in conté crayon, with red seal.

Translation of Hebrew from Jeremiah 9:1:   *"Oh that my head were waters and mine eyes a fountain of tears that I might weep day and night for the slain daughter of Israel."*

Shahn gives no specific reason for there being two versions of this subject.

24

מִי־יִתֵּן רֹאשִׁי מַיִם וְעֵינִי מְקוֹר דִּמְעָה
וְאֶבְכֶּה יוֹמָם וָלַיְלָה אֵת חַלְלֵי בַת־עַמִּי:

And mine eyes a fountain of tears

No. 5   ANDANTE, 1966

Serigraph, printed in black. Composition 16 1/2 x 23; sheet 21 x 26 1/2.
Unspecified edition size; signed in conté crayon, and red seal.

The drawing for this print was commissioned by the Olivetti Company.

## No. 6   BEATITUDE, 1955

Wood-engraving, printed in color, made by Leonard Baskin after a painting by Shahn. Composition 10 1/4 x 15 1/4; sheet 15 1/8 x 21. Edition of 400; signed lower left: "Ben Shahn," with a brush; lower right: "Leonard Baskin sculpsit," in pencil.

Published by The International Graphic Arts Society, Inc., New York. Although the print is entitled "Beatitudes" in pencil, its correct title is "Beatitude."

No. 7   BLIND BOTANIST, 1961

Serigraph, printed in black, with green lettering. Composition 38 x 23 1/2; sheet 40 x 26 1/4. Edition of 100, signed in black or red with a brush, and red seal.

Quotation from Robert Hooke's *Micrographia*, 1665:   *"So many are the links, upon which the true philosophy depends, of which, if one be loose or weak, the whole chain is in danger of being dissolved; it is to begin with the Hands and Eyes; and to proceed on through the memory, to be continued by the reason; nor is it to stop there, but to come to the Hands and Eyes again ..."*

*"Intensity of delving into science in its purity and the possible painful and contradictory results — the abuse and thwarting of the original dedication. The paradox — always a preoccupation, as in my painting,* The Red Stairway. *The paradox of man's goals."*   B.S.

So many are the links, upon which the true philosophy
depends, of which, if one be loose, or weak, the whole chain
and Eyes; and if proved dissolved, it is to begin with the Hands
continued by the reason through the memory, to be
not is it to stop the reason through the memory, to be
but to come to the
Hands and
Eyes again ...... Robert Hooke Micrographia. 1665.

Ben Shahn

No. 8   BLIND BOTANIST, 1963

Color lithograph. Composition 25 1/2 x 20; sheet 26 3/4 x 20 1/2. Edition about 200; signed in plate, lower left: "A. MANARANCHE GRAV. LITH.;" lower right: "Ben Shahn." Printed at Fernand Mourlot, Paris.

Printed from zinc plates.

Ben Shahn

No. 9  BOY ON A TRICYCLE, 1947

also called TRICYCLE ACROBAT

Serigraph, printed in black. Composition 11 5/8 x 8; on one-half of a double sheet 11 7/8 x 15; left hand side has printed text: *"A Merry Xmas and a Happy New Year."* Unspecified edition size; signed with a brush.

Issued as a Christmas card.

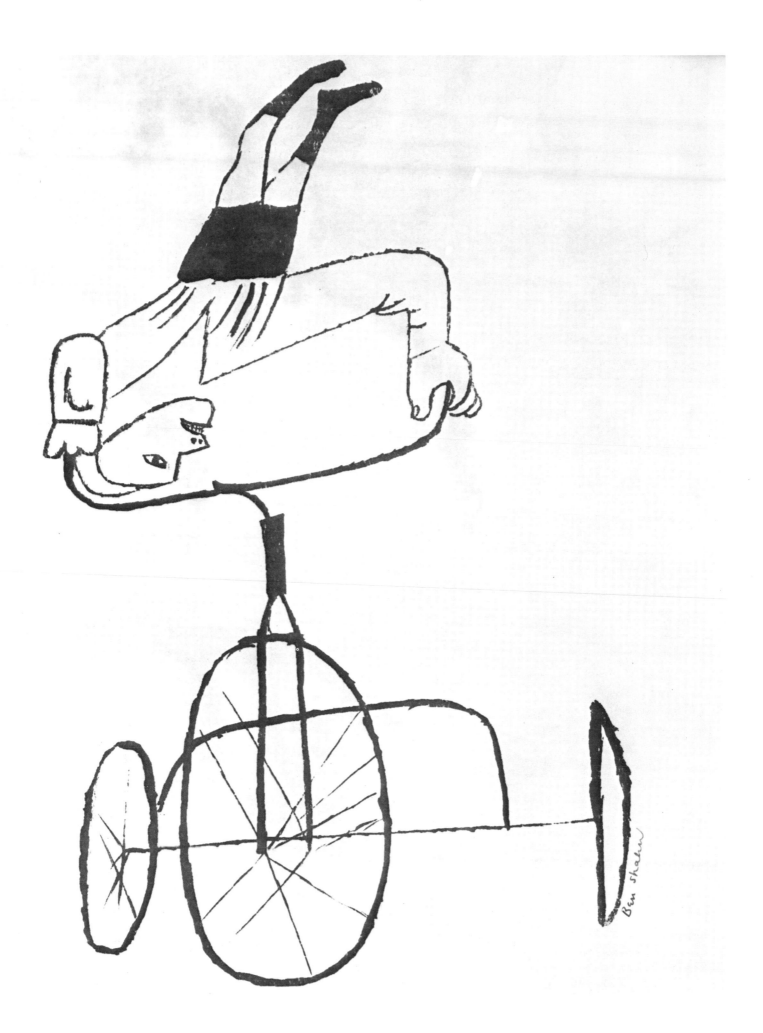

## No. 10   BRANCHES OF WATER OR DESIRE, 1965

Serigraph, printed in black. Composition 26 x 19; sheet 26 3/8 x 20 1/2. Unspecified edition size; signed in red with a brush, and red seal.

This subject was made at the request of Mrs. Cleve Gray for *Art in America* to illustrate a poem with this title by Alan Dugan.

## No. 11 BYZANTINE MEMORY, 1966

Serigraph, printed in black, with hand coloring. Composition 24 x 18 1/8; sheet 26 1/2 x 20 1/8. Unspecified edition size; signed in conté crayon, and red seal.

No. 12  CAT'S CRADLE, 1959

Serigraph, printed in blue and black. Composition 17 1/2 x 26 1/8; sheet 20 1/4 x 26 3/8. Unspecified edition size; signed with a red brush.

This subject was drawn directly on the silk screen, not traced from an existing drawing. There exist about 3 impressions printed without the water.

No. 13  CREDO (small), 1960

Serigraph, printed in black. Composition 13 3/4 x 19 3/4; sheet 16 1/2 x 22 3/4. Unspecified edition size; signed in red conté crayon.

Quotation from Martin Luther: *"I have the right to believe freely to be a slave to no mans authority   If this be heresy so be it   It is still the truth   To go against conscience is neither right nor safe   I cannot . . . will not . . . recant   Here I Stand   No man can command my conscience."*

This subject grew out of a request by the Lutheran Church to design a symbol for a button. The design showed Luther nailing his theses to the door of the Schlosskirche at Wittenberg. *Credo* evolved after further study of Luther.

I have the right to believe freely
to be a slave to no mans authority
If this be heresy so be it It is still
the truth To go against conscience is
neither right nor safe I cannot.....
will not..... recant HERE I stand
No man can command my conscience

No. 14  CREDO (large), 1966

Serigraph, printed in blue and black. Composition 24 1/4 x 19 3/4; sheet 26 1/4 x 21. Unspecified edition size; signed in conté crayon, and red seal.

The silk screen for *Credo* (small) superimposed on a book held by a man.

I have the right to believe freely
to be a slave to no man's authority
If this be heresy so be it. It is still
the truth. To go against conscience is
neither right nor safe. I cannot.....
will not..... recant. HERE I stand.
No man can command my conscience.

No. 15  DECALOGUE, 1961

Serigraph, printed in black, with hand coloring and applied gold leaf. Composition 37 1/4 x 24; sheet 40 1/4 x 26 1/4. Unspecified edition size; signed with a brush, and red seal.

The first letters of the Decalogue are indicated.

No. 16  DESERTED FAIR GROUND, ca. 1948

Serigraph, printed in colors. Composition 11 5/8 x 14 3/4; sheet 19 1/4 x 25 1/4. Unspecified edition size; signed "Ben Sh." in black in screen, "Ben Shahn" in red with a brush.

Issued as a Christmas gift to atone for not writing letters. Shahn, who loves deserted places such as beaches during the off-season, produced this subject after visiting a fair in Trenton, the day after it had closed.

No. 17   ECCLESIASTES, 1966

Serigraph, printed in black, with brown lettering. Composition 19 7/8 x 16 1/8; sheet 22 3/4 x 17 3/4. Unspecified edition size; signed in pencil, and red seal.

Quotation from Ecclesiastes 11:9: *"Rejoice, O young man, in thy youth; and let thy heart cheer thee in the days of thy youth, and walk in the ways of thine heart, and in the sight of thine eyes: but know thou, that for all these things God will bring thee into judgment."*

No. 17A   ECCLESIASTES, 1966 ( variant printing )

Shahn has made several impressions of this same print after partially cleaning the original screen with solvent. He hopes to be able to control this process which produces a rough, watery line.

שְׂמַח בָּחוּר בְּיַלְדוּתֶךָ וִיטִיבְךָ לִבְּךָ בִּימֵי בְּחוּרוֹתֶיךָ וְהַלֵּךְ בְּדַרְכֵי
לִבְּךָ וּבְמַרְאֵי עֵינֶיךָ וְדָע כִּי עַל־כָּל־אֵלֶּה יְבִיאֲךָ הָאֱלֹהִים בַּמִּשְׁפָּט

No. 18   4½ OUT OF EVERY 5,   1941

Serigraph, printed in colors. Composition 13 1/2 x 10 1/2; sheet 25 1/4 x 19 1/8. Unspecified edition size; signed with a brush.

Shahn has always given away impressions of this subject. It derives from the statistical expression: *"four and a half out of every five"* people have this or that. He had planned to do a print of a similar nature which was to be entitled *"Now Gentlemen, it is time for us to prey."*

No. 19  FUTILITY, 1960

Wood-engraving made by Stefan Martin after a drawing by Shahn. Composition 4 1/2 x 5 5/8; sheet 10 x 12 5/8. Edition of 300; signed lower left: "Ben Shahn," with a brush; lower right: "Ben Shahn" in plate, and "Stefan Martin sc." [sculpsit] in pencil.

Published by The International Graphic Arts Society, Inc., New York.

Ben Shahn                    Futility    25III/    Ben Shahn
                                           300      Silas Mortense

No. 20   GANDHI, 1965

Serigraph, printed in black. Composition 36 1/4 x 24 1/4; sheet 40 x 26. Unspecified edition size; signed with a brush, and red seal.

This subject first appeared as a drawing for *Look* magazine. A collotype version was later published ( see no. 67 ).

No. 21 THE HANDSHAKE, 1942
also called GREETING

Serigraph, printed in colors. Composition 15 x 22; sheet ca. 16 1/4 x 23. Unspecified edition size, ca. 20; unsigned.

This print was made in Washington, D. C. It represents no identifiable subjects. Shahn calls the handshake "dyspeptic."

No. 22   I THINK CONTINUALLY OF THOSE WHO WERE
TRULY GREAT, 1965

White and black silk screen lettering, and watercolor wash. Composition 24 1/2 x 20; sheet 26 1/2 x 21. Unspecified edition size; signed with brush, and red seal.

Lettered: "*Carol Denise McNair; William L. Moore; Cynthia Robertson; James L. Coley; Wesley Addie; Mae Collins; Jimie Lee Jackson; Viola Gregg Liuzza; Virgil L. Wade; Rev. James J. Reeb*" followed by a Stephen Spender poem, the first line of which is the title of this print:

"*Near the snow, near the sun. In the highest fields*
*see how these names are feted by the waving grass*
*and by the streamers of white cloud*
*and whispers of wind in the listening sky.*
*The names of those who in their lives fought for life*
*who wore at their hearts the fire's centre.*
*Born of the sun they traveled a short while towards the sun*
*and left the vivid air signed with their honor*"

This print is a tribute to civil rights martyrs. Each impression differs from the other because the dove is entirely created by outlining it with hand-applied watercolor wash. Only the text is silk-screened. The bird's beak is made by stamping with the tip of an art gum eraser.

There has been published a photo-offset lithographic reproduction of this subject, printed by the Meriden Gravure Company, Meriden, Connecticut. ( See no. 69d )

I THINK CONTINUALLY OF THOSE WHO WERE TRULY GREAT

Carol Denise McNair     William L. Moore
Cynthia Robertson     James L. Coley
L. June Lee     Addie Mae Collins
Jackson     Virgil L. Wade
Viola
Gregg     Rev. James
Liucco     J. Reeb

NEAR THE SNOW,
   NEAR THE SUN,
   IN THE HIGHEST FIELDS
SEE HOW THESE NAMES ARE FETED
   BY THE WAVING GRASS
   AND BY THE STREAMERS
   OF WHITE CLOUD
AND WHISPERS OF WIND
   IN THE LISTENING SKY.
THE NAMES OF THOSE
   WHO IN THEIR LIVES
   FOUGHT FOR LIFE
WHO WORE AT THEIR HEARTS
   THE FIRE'S CENTRE.
BORN OF THE SUN
   THEY TRAVELLED A SHORT WHILE
   TOWARDS THE SUN,
AND LEFT THE VIVID AIR SIGNED
   WITH THEIR HONOR.
                        STEPHEN SPENDER

Ben Shahn

No. 23  IMMIGRANT FAMILY, 1941

Serigraph, printed in colors. Composition 11 1/4 x 18; sheet 16 1/4 x 23. Unspecified edition size; unsigned.

Ben Shahn's first silk screen print.

No. 24   LEVANA, 1967

Lithograph, printed in black. Composition 21 3/4 x 14; sheet 30 x 22 1/8. Edition of 125, signed with a red brush, and red seal; also dry-stamp of Gemini G.E.L. ⅠⅠ and copyright mark ©.

This lithograph was printed by Gemini G.E.L., in Los Angeles, California from a transfer drawing by Shahn.

Artist Proof II                    Ben Shahn 1966

Nos. 25-34   LEVANA AND OUR LADIES OF SORROW,
1931

Ten lithographs, published in a blue buckram portfolio, 18 3/4 x 15, decorated with a picture of Levana and the title; sheet size 13 3/16 x 10, each print matted. Edition about 10; signed on stone, and in pencil. Published by Philip Stern.

No. 25   *"Behold what is greater than yourselves!"*
Composition 11 3/4 x 8.

No. 26   *. . . I saw (dimly relieved upon the dark background of my dreams) the imperfect lineaments of the awful Sisters.*
Composition 10 3/8 x 8.

No. 27   *Eternal silence reigns in their kingdoms.*
Composition 9 1/8 x 8.

No. 28   *Rachel weeping for her children and refusing to be comforted.*
Composition 11 3/4 x 8 1/8.

No. 29   *She it was that stood in Bethlehem on the night when Herod's sword swept its nurseries of Innocents.*
Composition 11 1/2 x 8 1/4.

"Behold what is greater than yourselves!"

..I saw (dimly relieved upon the dark background of
my dreams) the imperfect lineaments of the awful Sisters

Eternal silence reigns in their kingdoms

Rachel weeping for her children and refusing to be comforted.

She it was that stood in Bethlehem on the night when
Herod's sword swept its nurseries of Innocents.

No. 30   *Every slave that at noonday looks up to the tropical sun with timid reproach . . .*
Composition 11 3/4 x 7 1/4.

No. 31   *Every woman sitting in darkness . . .*
Composition 9 1/2 x 7 1/4.

No. 32   *She also is the mother of lunacies and the suggestress of suicides.*
Composition 10 3/4 x 7 3/4.

No. 33   *he worshipped the worm and prayed to the wormy grave.*
Composition 11 5/8 x 7 5/8.

No. 34   *. . . to plague his heart until we had unfolded the capacities of his spirit."*
Composition 7 3/8 x 11 1/4.

Of the original edition of this portfolio, only about 10 were sold; the remainder Shahn burned because they had sold so poorly.

Thomas De Quincey's dream prose, "Levana and Our Ladies of Sorrow," is from his *Suspira de Profundis, An Epilogue to Confessions of an English Opium Eater*.

Every slave that at noonday looks up to
the tropical sun with timid reproach...

Every woman sitting in darkness....

She also is the mother of lunacies
and the suggestress of suicides.

he worshipped the worm and prayed to the wormy grave.

.....to plague his heart until we had unfolded the capacities of his spirit"

## No. 35   LUTE AND MOLECULE, No. 1, 1958

Serigraph, printed in black, with hand coloring. Composition 25 x 38 3/4; sheet 27 1/2 x 40 1/2. Unspecified edition size; signed with a brush.

While at Harvard, Shahn was lent a *"marvelous model of a molecule"* by a noted chemist; and a lutanist also left his lute in his studio. *"The accidental juxtaposition intrigued me and I did a screen on that theme."* B.S.

## No. 35A   LUTE AND MOLECULE, No. 2, 1958

A version of no. 35 with different coloring.

## No. 35B   LUTE, 1957

Silk screen. Sheet 25 x 37.

There exists a unique serigraph of "Lute," done on brown paper. *"I was not satisfied with this one."*   B.S.

*35B*

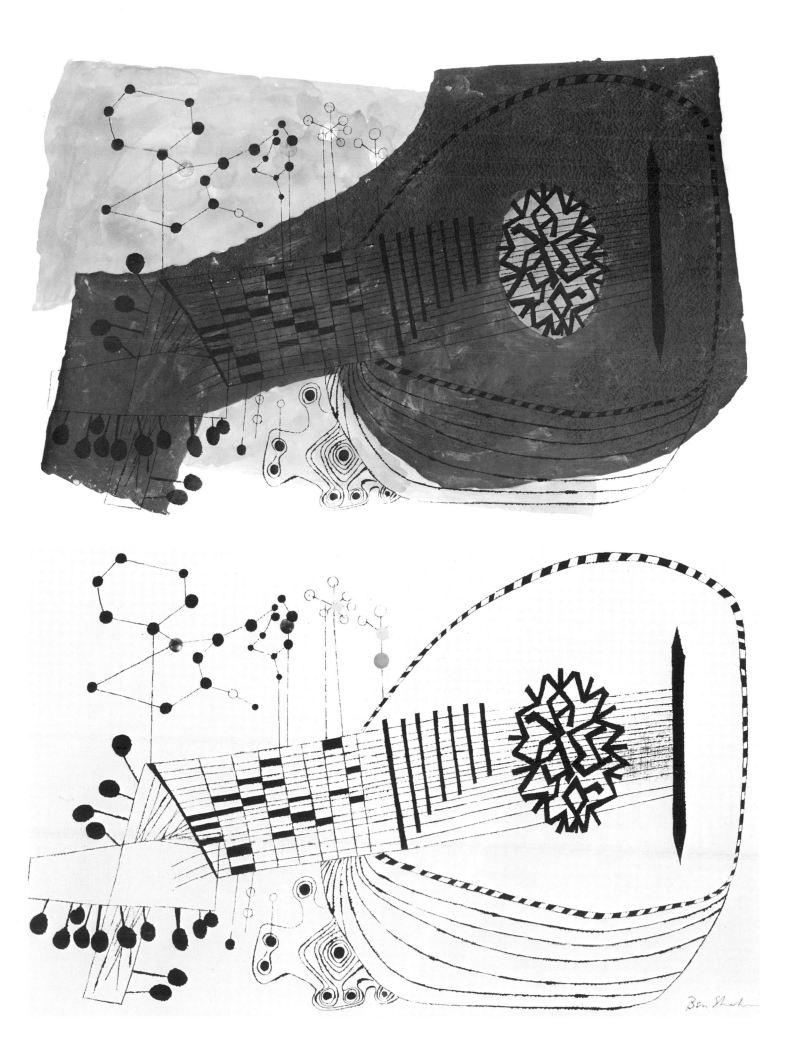

Ben Shahn

No. 36   MARTIN LUTHER KING, 1966

Wood-engraving made by Stefan Martin after a drawing by Shahn. Composition 18 3/4 x 15 1/4; sheet 25 x 20 1/8. Edition of 300; signed lower left: "Stefan Martin sc." [sculpsit] in pencil; lower right: "Ben Shahn," with a brush, and red seal.

Published by The International Graphic Arts Society, Inc., New York.

No. 37   MASK, 1959

Serigraph, printed in colors. Composition 26 1/4 x 19 1/2; sheet 26 1/2 x
20 1/2. Unspecified edition size; signed with a brush, and red seal.

*"The colors were suggested by a Sicilian pot that I once owned."*   B.S.

No. 38 MASK, 1963

Color lithograph. Composition 25 1/2 x 19 1/4; sheet 30 x 21. Edition about 200; signed in plate, lower left: "A. Manaranche Lith.," lower right: "Ben Shahn." Printed at Fernand Mourlot, Paris.

Printed from zinc plates.

No. 39   MAXIMUS OF TYRE, 1963

Serigraph, with hand coloring. Composition 35 x 25 1/2; sheet 36 x 26 3/4. Unspecified edition size; signed with a brush, and red seal.

Quotation from the closing paragraph of *Dissertatio VIII* by Maximus of Tyre, 1st century, A. D. *"God Himself, the Father and Fashioner of all that is, older than the sun or the sky, greater than time and eternity and all the flow of being, is unnameable by any lawgiver, unutterable by any voice, not to be seen by any eye. But we, being unable to apprehend His essence, use the help of sounds and names and pictures, of beaten gold and ivory and silver, of plants and rivers, mountain peaks and torrents, yearning for the knowledge of Him, and in our weakness naming all that is beautiful in this world after His nature — just as happens to earthly lovers. To them the most beautiful sight will be the actual lineaments of the beloved. But for remembrance sake they will be happy in the sight of a lyre, a little spear, a chair, perhaps, or a running ground, or anything in the world that wakens the memory of the beloved. Why should I further examine and pass judgment about images? Let men know what is divine. Let them know: that is all. If a Greek is stirred to the remembrance of God by the art of Pheidias, an Egyptian by paying worship to animals, another man by a river, another by fire . . . I have no anger for their divergences; only let them know. Let them love, let them remember."*

No. 39A   ALPHABET AND MAXIMUS, 1966

Serigraph, watercolor, and conté crayon rubbing. Sheet 37 x 26. Unique proof; signed with a brush, and red seal.

This unique print combines *Maximus of Tyre* ( no. 39 ) with *Alphabet of Creation* ( no. 3 ). Shahn made a cardboard cutout of *Alphabet* from which he made the rubbing.

GOD HIMSELF, THE FATHER AND FASHIONER OF ALL THAT IS, OLDER THAN THE SUN OR THE SKY, GREATER THAN TIME AND ETERNITY AND ALL THE FLOW OF BEING, IS UNNAMEABLE BY ANY LAWGIVER, UNUTTERABLE BY ANY VOICE, NOT TO BE SEEN BY ANY EYE. BUT WE, BEING UNABLE TO APPREHEND HIS ESSENCE, USE THE HELP OF SOUNDS AND NAMES AND PICTURES, OF BEATEN GOLD AND IVORY AND SILVER, OF PLANTS AND RIVERS, MOUNTAIN PEAKS AND TORRENTS, YEARNING FOR THE KNOWLEDGE OF HIM, AND IN OUR WEAKNESS NAMING ALL THAT IS BEAUTIFUL IN THIS WORLD AFTER HIS NATURE— JUST AS HAPPENS TO EARTHLY LOVERS. TO THEM THE MOST BEAUTIFUL SIGHT WILL BE THE ACTUAL LINEAMENTS OF THE BELOVED, BUT FOR REMEMBRANCE SAKE THEY WILL BE HAPPY IN THE SIGHT OF A LYRE, A LITTLE SPEAR, A CHAIR, PERHAPS, OR A RUNNING GROUND, OR ANYTHING IN THE WORLD THAT WAKENS THE MEMORY OF THE BELOVED. WHY SHOULD I FURTHER EXAMINE AND PASS JUDGEMENT ABOUT IMAGES? LET MEN KNOW WHAT IS DIVINE, LET THEM KNOW: THAT IS ALL. IF A GREEK IS STIRRED TO THE REMEMBRANCE OF GOD BY THE ART OF PHEIDIAS, AN EGYPTIAN BY PAYING WORSHIP TO ANIMALS, ANOTHER MAN BY A RIVER, ANOTHER BY FIRE, I HAVE NO ANGER FOR THEIR DIVERGENCES; ONLY LET THEM KNOW, LET THEM LOVE, LET THEM REMEMBER.

*Closing Paragraph of Dissertation VIII of Maximus of Tyre (2d Cent. A.D.)*

No. 40   MENORAH, 1965

Serigraph, printed in black, with hand coloring and applied gold leaf. Composition 23 5/8 x 19 1/8; sheet 26 1/2 x 20 5/8. Unspecified edition size; signed with a brush, and red seal.

In describing his interest in the Menorah, the *"earliest Hebrew symbol known,"* Shahn mentions that he first drew this subject for his book, *Alphabet of Creation,* then as a frontispiece for the *Haggadah,* and he has just completed a large representation of a Menorah in a design for stained glass.

No. 41   MINE BUILDING, 1956

Serigraph, printed in black, with hand coloring. Composition 17 x 28 7/8; Sheet 22 1/2 x 30 3/4. Unspecified edition size; signed with a brush.

This subject was evoked by *"the dismal and sick beauty that accrues to those dark sooty mine buildings that had once been painted, and that take on strange efflorescences."*   B.S.

Shahn's daughter, Suzie, helped to color this edition. See note on coloring of *Phoenix* ( no. 45 ).

## No. 42 PASSION OF SACCO AND VANZETTI, 1958

Serigraph, figures in black, text in brown. Composition 25 3/4 x 17 1/2; sheet 30 1/4 x 22 3/4. Unspecified edition size; signed with a brush.

Quotation from Bartolomeo Vanzetti: *"If it had not been for these thing, I might have live out my life talking at street corners to scorning men. I might have die, unmarked, unknown a failure. Now we are not a failure. This is our career and our triumph. Never in our full life could we hope to do such work for tolerance, for joostice, for man's onderstanding of man as now we do by accident. Our words — our lives — our pains nothing! The taking of our lives — lives of a good shoemaker and a poor fish peddler — all! That last moment belongs to us — that agony is our triumph."*

These were the words of Bartolomeo Vanzetti, as taken verbatim in shorthand by Philip Strong, shortly before the execution of the two men, Sacco and Vanzetti. Nicola Sacco, a shoemaker, and Bartolomeo Vanzetti, a fish peddler, were charged with the robbery and murder of the paymaster and a guard of a shoe factory in South Braintree, Massachusetts, on April 15, 1920. Both the accused men were Italians who had emigrated to the U. S. in 1908. Despite contradictory evidence and petitions for justice from around the world, they were executed on August 23, 1927.

## No. 42A IMMORTAL WORDS, 1958

Serigraph, printed in black. Composition 13 x 17 1/2; sheet 15 5/8 x 20 3/8. Unspecified edition size; signed with a brush.

This is a printing of the text only from no. 42.

## No. 42B PORTRAIT OF SACCO AND VANZETTI, 1958

Serigraph, printed in black. Composition 12 1/2 x 16. Unspecified edition size; signed with a brush.

This is a printing of the two portraits only from no. 42.

IF IT HAD NOT BEEN FOR THESE THING,
I MIGHT HAVE LIVE OUT MY LIFE TALK-
ING AT STREET CORNERS TO SCORN-
ING MEN. I MIGHT HAVE DIE, UN-
MARKED, UNKNOWN A FAILURE. NOW
WE ARE NOT A FAILURE. THIS IS OUR
CAREER AND OUR TRIUMPH. NEVER IN
OUR FULL LIFE COULD WE HOPE TO
DO SUCH WORK FOR TOLERANCE, FOR
JOOSTICE, FOR MAN'S ONDERSTANDING
OF MAN AS NOW WE DO BY ACCIDENT.
OUR WORDS-OUR LIVES-OUR PAINS
NOTHING! THE TAKING OF OUR LIVES-
LIVES OF A GOOD SHOEMAKER AND A
POOR FISH PEDDLER-ALL! THAT LAST
MOMENT BELONGS TO US- THAT
AGONY IS OUR TRIUMPH.

No. 43   PATERSON  (color version ), 1953

Serigraph, printed in black, with hand coloring by stencil. Composition 29 3/4 x 22; sheet 31 x 22 1/4. Edition of 60; signed in pencil.

*Paterson* is a print associated with some of Shahn's studies for the painting of that title. Having been to Paterson, New Jersey, Shahn was fascinated by the dyeing patterns in the windows.

No. 44    PATERSON ( black and white version ), 1953

Serigraph, printed in black. Composition 30 x 22 1/2; sheet 32 x 22 7/8. Unspecified edition size; signed with a brush.

See comment on no. 43.

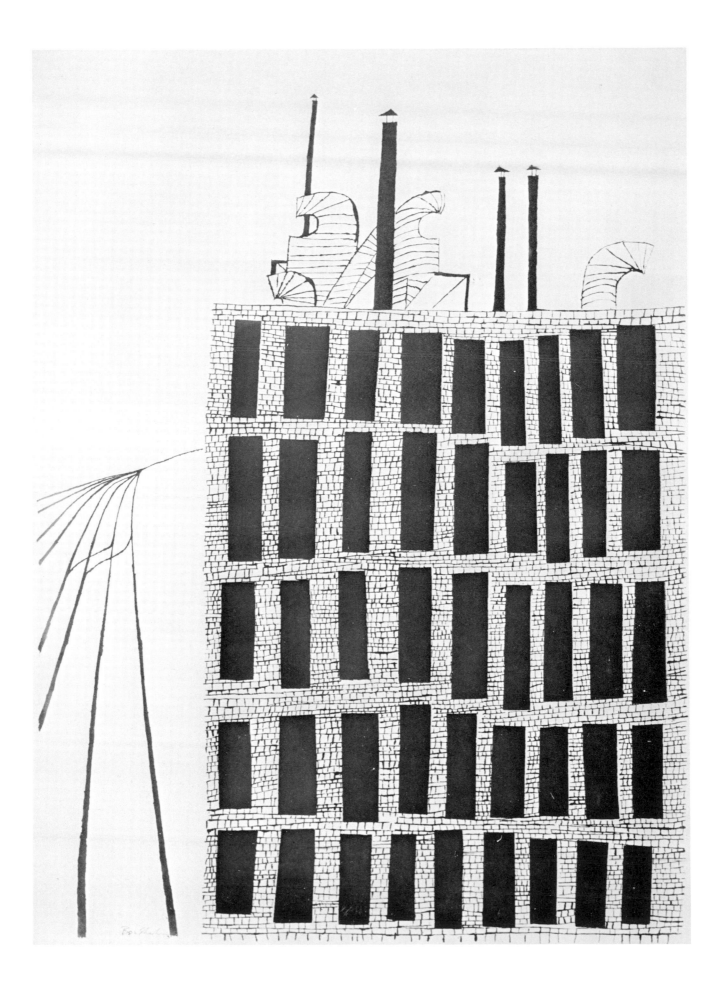

## No. 45   PHOENIX, 1952

Serigraph, printed in black, with hand coloring. Composition 22 5/8 x 21 3/8; sheet 30 3/4 x 22 5/8. Edition of 100; signed with a brush.

*"This was the first of those prints that I made (and make) in which I painted in color and then printed an image in black, registering that with the colors painted. This was to obtain a richness that I felt could not be achieved through simple color printing. The original painting for the* Phoenix *was done as a poster for an exhibition of mine."*   B.S.

*Mine Building* ( no. 41 ) and *Triple Dip* ( no. 58 ) were also colored this way. The coloring of *Phoenix* was entirely done by Shahn himself.


## No. 45A   PHOENIX

Identical serigraph, printed in black only. Edition of 50.

No. 46 PLEIADES, 1960

Serigraph, printed in gray and black, with hand coloring and applied gold leaf. Composition 18 1/8 x 24 3/4, sheet 20 3/8 x 26 1/2. Unspecified edition size; signed with a brush.

Quotation from *Job* 38:31-38: *"Canst thou bind the sweet influences of Pleiades, or loose the bands of Orion? Canst thou bring forth Mazzaroth in his season? or canst thou set the guide Arcturus with his sons? Knowest thou the ordinances of heaven? canst thou set the dominions thereof in the earth? Canst thou lift up thy voice to the clouds, that abundance of waters may cover thee? Canst thou send lightnings, that they may go, and say unto thee, Here are we? Who hath put wisdom in the inward parts? or who hath given understanding to the heart? Who can number the clouds in wisdom? or who can stay the bottles of heaven, when the dust groweth into hardness, and the clods cleave fast together?"*

*"The image and words arose in connection with masks that I drew for Archibald MacLeish for his play 'J. B.' They were made into sculpture by James Kearns."* B.S.

In speaking of this print Shahn remarked that, whereas scientists present their own theories regarding the origins of life, when Job was unconsoled he challenged God himself.

Shahn's son Jonathan helped to color this print.

התקשר מעדנות כימה או משכות
כסיל חפתה תהצא מזלות בעתו ועש על
בניה תנחם הידעת חקות שמים אם תשים משטרו
בארץ התרים לעב קולל ושפעת מים תכסד החשלה
ברקים וילכו ויאמרו לך הנו מי שת בטחות חכמה או
מי נתן לשכוי בינה מי יספר שחקים בחכמה ונבלי
שמים מי ישכיב בצקת עפר למוצק ורגבים ידבקו

*Ben Shahn*

## No. 47   POET, 1960

Serigraph, printed in two shades of brown. Composition 39 1/2 x 26; sheet 40 1/4 x 27 1/4. Unspecified edition size; signed with a brush.

## No. 47A   FRAGMENT OF THE POET'S BEARD, ca. 1960

Serigraph, printed in brown. Composition 7 1/4 x 21; sheet 18 3/8 x 25 5/8. Edition of 1 or 2, signed with a brush, and red seal.

Shahn made one or two of these impressions from a small portion of the screen used in *Poet*.

Ben Shahn

No. 48   PRAISE HIM WITH PSALTERY AND HARP, 1963

Serigraph, printed in black. Composition 23 1/4 x 18; sheet 23 3/4 x 24 1/4. Edition of about 150 or 200; signed variously with conté crayon, and red seal.

This print was made for the Benrus Watch Company. The title derives from the third verse of *Psalm 150*.

No. 49   PRENATAL CLINIC, 1941
also called MATERNITY CLINIC

Serigraph, printed in colors. Composition 14 1/2 x 21 3/4; sheet 15 1/4 x 22 1/2. Unspecified edition size; signed with a brush.

Lettered: *"Do I Deserve Prenatal Care"* and *"23 Gynecology Obstetrics."*

*"One of my earliest ventures in silk screen printing."*   B.S.

No. 50   PROFILE, 1952

Serigraph, printed in black and brown. Composition 25 x 20; sheet 38 3/4 x 25 1/2. Edition of 97; signed with a brush, and red seal.

To transfer a drawing onto a painting, Shahn rubs the back of the drawing with conté crayon. He has reproduced that effect in *Profile*. The print also exists in black outline only.

03-07

No. 51    PSALM 133, 1960

also called SONG OF DEGREES

Serigraph, printed in color. Composition 19 3/4 x 26 1/4; sheet 20 1/2 x
26 3/4. Unspecified edition; signed with a brush.

Lettered: Quotation from *Psalm 133*: *"Behold, how good and how
pleasant it is for breathren to dwell together in unity It is like the precious ointment upon the head, that ran down upon the beard, even
Aaron's beard: that went down to the skirts of his garments; As the dew
of Hermon, and as the dew that descended upon the mountains of Zion:
for there the Lord commanded the blessing, even life forevermore."*

There was published, in 1963, a photo-offset lithograph reproduction of
this subject, in an edition of 200 copies for Artists, Inc., New York City,
printed by The Meriden Gravure Company, Meriden, Connecticut,
which reproduces Shahn's signature and red seal. Composition 12 x 9;
sheet 22 1/4 x 16 3/4. ( See also no. 69c )

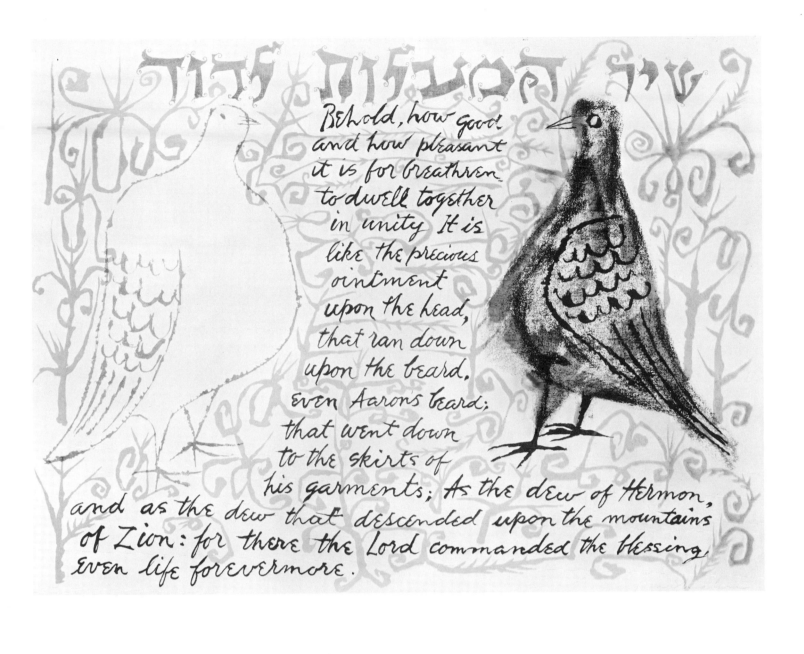

שיר המעלות לדוד

Behold, how good
and how pleasant
it is for breathren
to dwell together
in unity It is
like the precious
ointment
upon the head,
that ran down
upon the beard,
even Aarons beard:
that went down
to the skirts of
his garments; As the dew of Hermon,
and as the dew that descended upon the mountains
of Zion: for there the Lord commanded the blessing,
even life forevermore.

No. 52    PSALM 133, 1963
also called SONG OF DEGREES

Color lithograph. Composition 19 3/4 x 26; sheet 20 5/8 x 27. Edition about 200; signed in plate, lower left: "A. MANARANCHE GRAV. LITH.;" lower right, "Ben Shahn." Printed at Fernand Mourlot, Paris.

*"A hopeless pleading for people to get together."*    B.S.

Printed from zinc plates.

Behold, how good and how pleasant it is for breathren to dwell together in unity It is like the precious ointment upon the head, that ran down upon the beard, even Aarons beard; that went down to the skirts of his garments; As the dew of Hermon, and as the dew that descended upon the mountains of Zion: for there the Lord commanded the blessing, even life forevermore.

Ben Shahn

No. 53 SCIENTIST, 1957

Serigraph, printed in black, with hand coloring. Composition 8 7/8 x 6 1/4; sheet 9 x 7. Unspecified edition size; signed with a brush.

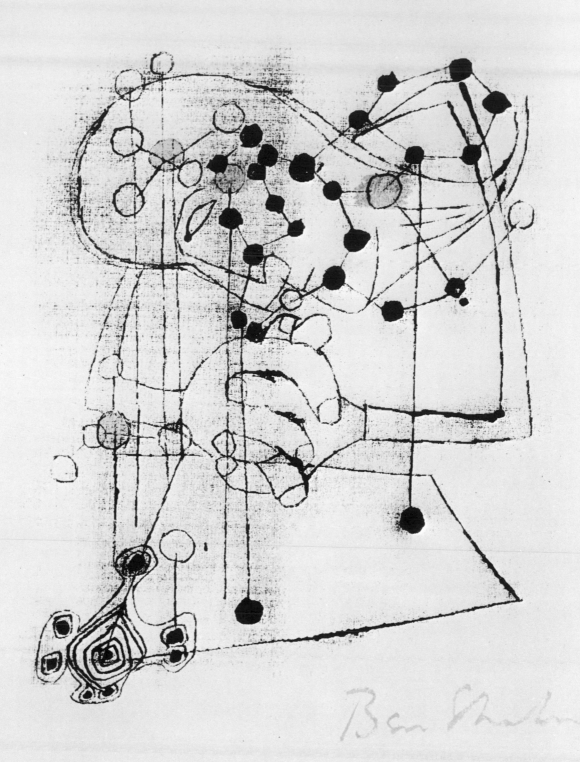

Ben Shahn

No. 54  SEWARD PARK, 1936

Color lithograph. Composition 11 7/8 x 17 7/8. Unspecified edition size; unsigned.

Made for the Resettlement Administration.

No. 55   SILENT MUSIC, 1950
also called MUSICAL CHAIRS

Serigraph, printed in black. Composition 17 1/4 x 35 1/4; sheet 25 1/2 x 39. Edition of 97; signed at left: "Ben Shahn," with a brush; at right: "Ben Shahn" in screen.

Once humourously referred to by Shahn as *Local 802 on strike.* This was the first print issued by Shahn in a numbered edition. Its origin was a drawing made for the Columbia Broadcasting System.

97/55  Ben Shahn

No. 56  SKOWHEGAN, 1965

Wood-engraving made by Stefan Martin after a drawing by Shahn. Composition 9 1/2 x 8 3/8; sheet 16 1/4 x 12. Unspecified edition size; signed at lower left: "Stefan Martin sc." [sculpsit] in pencil; at lower right: "Ben Shahn," in conté crayon, and red seal.

*"The print is called (for want of any other title) 'Skowhegan,' the reason being that it was made for the joint benefit of the Skowhegan School and Lenox-Hill Hospital."*   B.S.

Stefan Martin sc.

Ben Shahn

No. 57   SUPERMARKET, 1957

Serigraph, printed in black, and hand coloring. Composition 17 x
38 1/4; sheet 25 1/2 x 38 3/4. Unspecified edition size; signed with a
brush. Some impressions have been hand-colored.

*"To me, this print*, Supermarket, *along with the ones called* Silent Music, TV Antennae, *and the print called* Wheat Field, *are among the
abiding symbols of American daily life, to be celebrated and brought
into awareness."*   B.S.

No. 58   TRIPLE DIP, 1952

Serigraph, printed in black, with hand coloring. Composition 29 1/8 x 20 3/4; sheet 30 7/8 x 22 1/2. Edition of 58; signed with a brush.

This subject was drawn directly onto the screen, not traced from an existing drawing. See note on coloring of *Phoenix* ( no. 45 ).

8-58                                                                    Ben Shahn

No. 59   TV ANTENNAE, 1953
also called CALABANES

Serigraph, printed in black. Composition 16 1/4 x 36 3/4; sheet 25 1/2 x
39. Edition of 100; signed with a brush.

This print has sometimes been called *Calabanes*, a title suggested by a
misguided punster who envisioned some connection between TV Aerials, and Ariel and Caliban in Shakespeare's *The Tempest*.

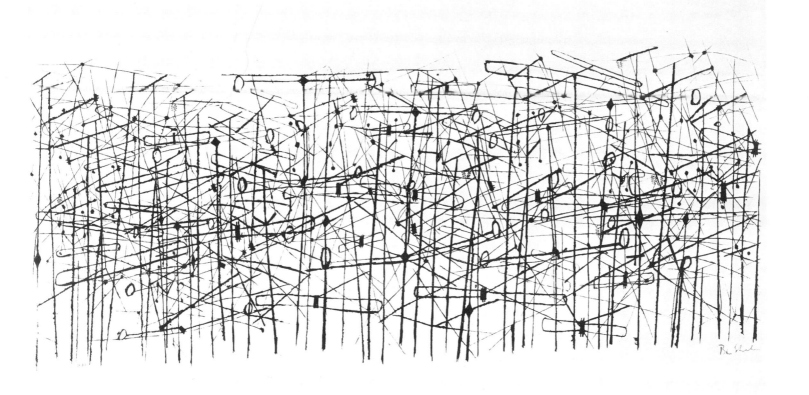

No. 60   VANDENBERG, DEWEY, AND TAFT, 1941
also called THREE FRIENDS

Serigraph, printed in colors. Composition 15 x 22 1/8; sheet 19 1/4 x
25 3/8. Unspecified edition size, ca. 20; signed with a brush.

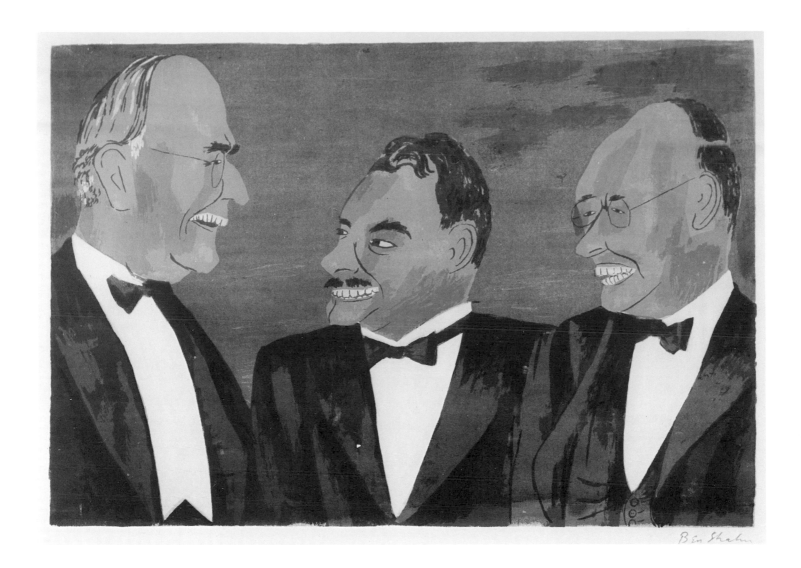

Ben Shahn

No. 61 WARSAW 1943, 1963

Serigraph, printed in black. Composition 33 1/2 x 24; sheet 37 x 28. Edition of 97; signed with a brush, and red seal.

Quotation from a 13th Century Yom Kippur prayer: "*These martyrs I will remember and my soul is torn with sorrow. In the days of our trials there is no one to help us.*"

"*Made to commemorate the 20th anniversary of the date of the destruction of Warsaw.*" B.S.

No. 61A ALPHABET AND WARSAW, 1966

Serigraph, watercolor, and conté crayon rubbing. Sheet 35 x 24. Unique proof; signed with a brush, and red seal.

Compare with *Alphabet and Maximus* (no. 39A).

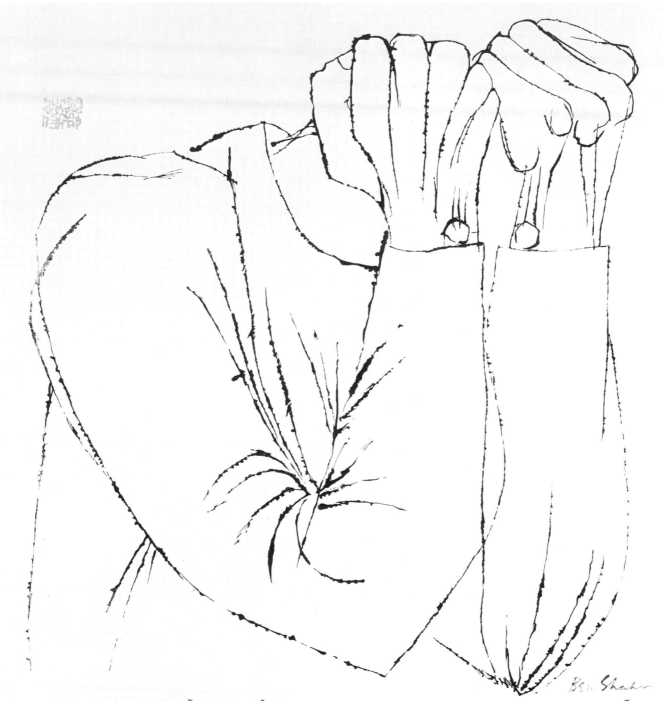

אלה אזכרה ונפשי עלי אשפכה
כי בלעונו זרים כעונה בלי
הפוכה כי בימי השר לא
עלתה ארוכה להרוגי מרוכה

No. 62   WHEAT FIELD, 1958

Serigraph, printed in black, with hand coloring. Composition 20 x 35 1/4; sheet 27 1/8 x 40 1/8. Unspecified edition size; signed with a brush.

No. 63  WHERE THERE IS A BOOK THERE IS NO
SWORD, 1950

Serigraph, printed in black. Composition 14 x 11; sheet 21 x 14. Edition of about 300; after many were given away, Shahn numbered the remaining 145; signed with a brush.

Literal translation: *"Where the sword is the book is not."* From the Talmud.

אִישׁ פַּסְיָא

לֵא פְּבַדְצַר

145/17 Ben Kahn

## No. 64 WILFRED OWEN, 1956

Wood-engraving by Leonard Baskin after a drawing by Ben Shahn. Composition 8 x 4 1/4; sheet 11 5/8 x 9 1/4. Edition of 400; signed lower left: "Ben Shahn," in pencil; lower right: "Leonard Baskin, sculpt.," in pencil.

Frontispiece to the book *Thirteen Poems* by Wilfred Owen, 1956, published by The Gehenna Press, Northampton, Massachusetts.

## No. 65 FRONTISPIECE TO *HAGGADAH*, 1966

Lithograph, hand colored with stencils and applied gold leaf. Composition 13 3/4 x 10 on each side of a double fold 15 3/8 x 23 1/2. Edition of 292; signed with a brush, and red seal.

Frontispiece to the deluxe edition of *Haggadah*, 1966, printed in original lithography from stones by the Imprimerie Mourlot, Paris, with additional colors applied by hand through stencils.

Ben Shahn     *Leonard Baskin sculpt.*

הגדה של פסח
העתיק וצייר
בנימין שאן
עם תרגום
מבוא והערות
מאת בצלאל רות
פריז
דפוס טריאנון
שנה תשכ״ד

בְּרוּךְ אַתָּה יי אֱלֹהֵינוּ מֶלֶךְ הָעוֹלָם
שֶׁהֶחֱיָנוּ וְקִיְּמָנוּ וְהִגִּיעָנוּ לַזְּמַן הַזֶּה

Ben Shahn

*MONOTYPE:*

No. 66   THREE-PENNY OPERA, 1958

Monotype. Composition 28 x 22. Unique; signed lower right corner.

130

*REPRODUCTION:*

No. 67   GANDHI, 1965

Collotype reproduction of a drawing by Shahn. Composition 31 1/2 x 21; sheet 38 1/2 x 25. Edition of 200; printed signature.

Quotation from Mark Twain's *Mysterious Stranger*: *"There has never been a just one, never an honorable one — on the part of the instigator of the war. I can see a million years ahead, and this rule will never change in so many as half a dozen instances. The loud little handful — as usual — will shout for the war. The pulpit will — warily and cautiously — object — at first; the great big, dull bulk of the nation will rub its sleepy eyes and try to make out why there should be war, and will say, earnestly and indignantly, 'It is unjust and dishonorable, and there is no necessity for it.' Then the handful will shout louder. A few fair men on the other side will argue and reason against the war, with speech and pen, and at first will have a hearing and be applauded; but it will not last long; those others will outshout them, and presently the anti-war audience will thin out and lose popularity. Before long you will see this curious thing: the speakers stoned from the platform and free speech strangled by hordes of furious men who in their secret hearts are still at one with the stoned speakers — as earlier — but do not dare to say so. And now — the whole nation — pulpit and all — will take up the war cry, and shout itself hoarse, and mob any honest man who ventures to open his mouth; and presently such mouths will cease to open. Next the statesman will invent cheap lies, put the blame upon the nation that is attacked; and every man will be glad of those conscience-soothing falsities, and will diligently study them, and refuse to examine any refutations of them; and thus he will by and by — convince himself that the war is just, and will thank you for the better sleep he enjoys after this process of grotesque self-deception."*

Printed by The Meriden Gravure Company, Meriden, Connecticut.

THERE has never been a just one, never an honorable one-
on the part of the instigator of the war. I can see
a million years ahead, and this rule will never change
in so many as half a dozen instances.
The loud little handful - as usual will shout
for the war. The pulpit will - warily and cautiously
object - at first; the great big, dull bulk of the nation
will rub its sleepy eyes and try to make out
why there should be war, and will say,
earnestly and indignantly, "It is unjust and
dishonorable, and there is no necessity for it."
Then the handful will shout louder. A few fair
men on the other side will argue and reason
against the war with speech and pen,
and at first will have a hearing and be
applauded; but it will not last long; those others
will outshout them, and presently the anti-war
audience will thin out and lose popularity.
Before long you will see this curious thing:
the speakers stoned from the platform, and
free speech strangled by hordes of furious men
who in their secret hearts are still at one
with those stoned speakers as earlier - but
do not dare to say so. And now the whole
nation - pulpit and all - will take up the war-cry,
and shout itself hoarse, and mob
any honest man who ventures to open his mouth;
and presently such mouths will cease to open.
Next the statesman will invent cheap lies,
putting the blame upon the nation that is attacked,
and every man will be glad of those
conscience-soothing falsities, and will diligently
study them, and refuse to examine any refutations of them; and thus he will by and by
convince himself that the war is just,
and will thank God for the better
sleep he enjoys after this process
of grotesque self-deception.

Ben Shahn

*REPRODUCTION:*

No. 68  GOLDWATER, 1964. ( He Says No to Civilization and Survival )

Photo silk screen reproduction of a drawing by Shahn. Sheet size 28 x 22. Edition 500.

Quotations from *Goldwater: "I can tell you one thing and you can tell someone else what I said, but in the meantime I can turn around and deny it and all you can do is call me a damn liar." "Well I think it was the Germans that originated this modern concept of peace through strength." "I'd drop a low-yield atomic bomb on Chinese lines in North Vietnam, or maybe shell 'em with the Seventh Fleet." "But defoliation of the forests by low-yield atomic weapons could well be done." "That word brinkmanship is a great word." "I've been against it [foreign economic aid] for years, and I'll vote against it this year, too." "As for those who fear military men, I say fear the civilians — they're taking over." " If we could give the NATO command the right to decide when to use nuclear weapons, we could bring a third to half of our troops home." "The United States should resume U2 flights over Soviet territory." "Like a three dollar bill it's a phony." "There's no way to enforce civil rights." "I know one chapter [of the John Birch Society] the one in my home town. They are the finest people in my community." "They [the John Birch Society] believe in the Constitution, they believe in God, they believe in Freedom." "These people who constitute the extreme right are good people. They are generally fairly well-to-do people. They are very sincere in their beliefs." "You know, I haven't got a really first-class brain." "Our right of property is probably our most sacred right." "I think T.V.A. should be turned over to free enterprise even if they could only get one dollar for it." "Let's leave it up to the States." "It's their baby." "[Both parties] made a mistake in trying to be specific about civil rights [in their 1960 platforms]." "Let welfare be a private concern. Let it be promoted by individuals and families, by churches, private hospitals, religious service organizations, community charities and other institutions that have been established for this purpose." "When you say to Johnny 'Don't worry about the old man or your mother, we're going to take care of them when they get older,' you've destroyed there, the freedom of responsibility." "The inescapable and most harmful by-products of such operations as relief, social security, collective bargaining and public housing has been the weakening of the individual personality and of self-reliance." "The child has no right to an education. In most cases, the children will get along very well without it." "The United States is a Republic and not a Democracy." "Get rid of the graduated income tax." "Sometimes I think this country would be better off if we could just saw off the eastern seaboard and let it float out to sea."*

134

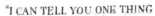

HE SAYS NO TO CIVILIZATION AND SURVIVAL
HE VOTED AGAINST
NUCLEAR TEST BAN
CIVIL RIGHTS ACT
TAX REDUCTION
MEDICAL CARE FOR THE AGED
MINIMUM WAGE LEGISLATION

SAY NO TO THE NO-SAYER
**VOTE JOHNSON**

NO. 68A

There also exists a similar subject, commercially reproduced, without
as much text. Sheet size 28 x 22. Edition 500.

*PORTFOLIO OF REPRODUCTIONS:*

No. 69   NINE DRAWINGS BY BEN SHAHN, 1965

Nine photo-offset lithograph reproductions of Shahn's drawings, issued in gray buckram portfolio, 22 3/4 x 17 3/4, with signature of Ben Shahn in white, on cover, including a poem by Edwin Rosskam. Edition of 300, published by the Laywers Constitutional Defense Committee of the American Civil Liberties Union. One print has been signed by the artist in each portfolio. Titles are printed in burnt sienna, each sheet measures 22 x 16 3/8:

a.   Thou Shalt Not Stand Idly By
b.   Rev. Martin Luther King ( See no. 36 )
c.   Behold How Good and How Pleasant ( See no. 51 )
d.   I Think Continually of Those Who Were Truly Great ( See no. 22 )
e.   We Shall Overcome
f.   Frederick Douglass ( See also no. 71 )
g.   James Chaney ( See also no. 70 )
h.   Michael Schwerner ( See also No. 70 )
i.   Andrew Goodman ( See also no. 70 )

Most of the sheets are stamped in green, verso: *"Copyright 1965 by Ben Shahn."*

Printed by The Meriden Gravure Company, Meriden, Connecticut.

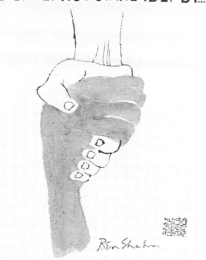

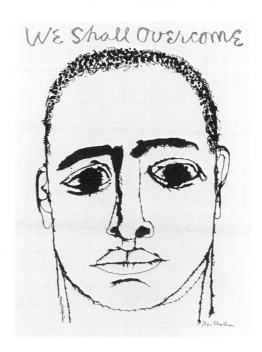

No. 70   MICHAEL SCHWERNER, ANDREW GOODMAN, JAMES CHANEY, 1965

Three photo silk screen reproductions of Shahn's drawings, issued in plain blue paper wrapper, 22 1/2 x 17 1/2, signed and numbered by the artist, including a printed martyrology by Edwin Rosskam. Edition of 300, published by the Human Relations Council of Greater New Haven, Connecticut. Titles are printed in raw umber, each sheet measures 21 7/8 x 16 3/4. See also nos. 69 g, h, i, where these same portraits, with titles printed in burnt sienna, were issued by the Lawyers Constitutional Defense Committee of the American Civil Liberties Union.

These three young men were killed in Mississippi during the summer of 1964.

MICHAEL SCHWERNER

ANDREW GOODMAN

JAMES CHANEY

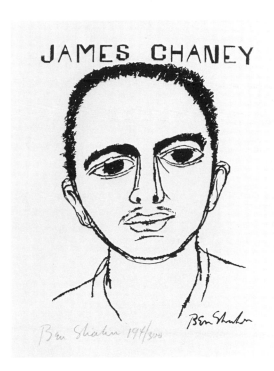

*PORTFOLIO OF REPRODUCTIONS:*

## No. 71   FREDERICK DOUGLASS, 1965

Four photo silk screen reproductions of Shahn's drawings, signed by the artist. Edition of 250, published by the Museum of African Art, Frederick Douglass Institute of Negro Arts and History, Washington, D. C. Titles are printed in raw umber, each sheet measures 22 x 16 3/4.

Shahn has pictured Frederick Douglass ( 1817?-1895 ), editor, author, abolitionist, at four stages in his life. Douglass rose from slavery to become United States Minister to Haiti.

FREDERICK DOUGLASS

FREDERICK DOUGLASS

FREDERICK DOUGLASS

FREDERICK DOUGLASS

No. 72    LAISSEZ-FAIRE ( Les Affaires )

Silk screen, printed in colors. Composition 8 3/4 x 16 1/2; sheet 17 3/4 x 24 1/2. Edition of 250?, signed in screen and lower right, with copyright symbol.

*"The title, substituted in parentheses, is as phony as are the prints being sold by an unauthorized printmaker. What happened was that the original print, entitled 'Laissez-faire' was authorized by me to be made by two competent young printmakers. They went out of business and sold their screens to another printmaker who has been printing them horribly and selling them without any authorization from me whatever — not to mention, without any payments whatever."*    B.S.


No. 73    SILENT NIGHT

Silk screen, printed in black. Edition of 200, numbered and signed.

( See comment on no. 72 ) *"This was the other print so pirated."*    B.S.

# A Partial List of Published Books

1. THE ALPHABET OF CREATION. An Ancient Legend from the Zohar, with drawings by Ben Shahn. New York, Pantheon, 1954.

   11 x 7. 44 pp.

   Edition: 50 copies, numbered 1-50 on Umbria paper, including an original drawing. 500 copies, numbered 51-550 on Rives paper, all signed, in slipcase.

   The Alphabet of Creation is one of the legends from the *Sefer Ha-Zohar*, or Book of Splendor, an ancient Gnostic work, written in Aramaic by a thirteenth century Spanish scholar named Moses de Leon. This is a rather free adaptation by Ben Shahn from the English translation of Maurice Samuel and other sources.

2. THE BIOGRAPHY OF A PAINTING, by Ben Shahn. Harvard University, Fogg Museum, 1956 ( Fogg Picture Books, No. 6 ).

   5 3/16 x 7 5/8. 32 pp. illustrated.

3. THE BIOGRAPHY OF A PAINTING, by Ben Shahn. New York, Paragraphic Books; and Fitz Henry and Whiteside, Ltd., Canada, 1966.

   10 7/8 x 8 3/8. 104 pp. illustrated.

   This is the same text as above, but far more profusely illustrated.

4. A BOY OF OLD PRAGUE, by Ish-Kishor, drawings by Ben Shahn. New York, Pantheon Books, 1963.

   9 1/4 x 6 1/4. 90 pp.

144

5. ECCLESIASTES OR, THE PREACHER, in the King James translation of the Bible, with drawings by Ben Shahn, engraved in wood by Stefan Martin. Calligraphy by David Soshensky. New York, Spiral Press, 1965.

13 1/8 x 9 7/8. 35 pp. illustrated; in gray slipcase.

Edition: 285 numbered copies.

6. HAGGADAH FOR PASSOVER [Deluxe edition]. Copied and illustrated by Ben Shahn. With a translation, introduction, and notes by Cecil Roth. Paris, Trianon Press, 1966.

15 3/4 x 12 in parchment-covered box with brass clasps and gold lettering 17 x 13. XXIV, 935 pp., 12 color illustrations and double title page.

*"This first edition . . . consists of 292 copies bearing the Artist's signature and cypher on the frontispiece."*

Edition: 18 copies, numbered i to xviii are *hors commerce.* 10 copies, numbered A to J, each containing one of the Artist's original illustrations of *"An Only Kid,"* are printed on Auvergne handmade pure rag paper. They include two extra sets of the color plates, one on Japanese Nacré . . . and the other on Arches Grand Vélin; one set of the plates left uncolored, on Arches Vergé paper, a series of progressives showing the stages in hand-stencil coloring of a single plate, together with three of the original guide sheets and stencils; and two proof states of the lithograph frontispiece. 16 copies, numbered K to Z . . . on Arches Grand Vélin pure rag paper. They include an extra set of the color plates on Auvergne . . ., a set of plates left uncolored on Arches Vergé . . .; three of the original guide sheets and stencils; and two proof states of the lithograph frontispiece. 20 copies, numbered I to XX are printed on Arches Grand Vélin pure rag paper. They include an extra set of the color plates on Arches Vergé paper, a set of the plates left uncolored, on Arches Vergé and a proof state of the lithograph frontispiece. 228 copies, numbered 1-228 are printed on pure rag Arches Vergé paper especially manufactured to match the paper used by the artist.

The reproduction in facsimile of the artist's originals was done in Paris under his supervision. The illuminated pages were reproduced by collotype and hand-stencil in the workshop of MM. Hourdebaigt and Crampe under the direction of Trianon Press (France). Collotype was also used to reproduce the illustrations of *"An Only Kid."* The frontispiece and title page were drawn by the artist and printed in original lithography from stones by the

Imprimerie Mourlot, with additional colors applied by hand through stencils.

7. HOMMAGE TO MISTRESS BRADSTREET, by John Berryman, with pictures by Ben Shahn. New York, Farrar, Straus & Cudahy, 1956.

9 1/2 x 6 7/8. 57 pp.

8. INSIDE KASRILEVKE, by Sholom Aleichem, with pictures by Ben Shahn. New York, Schocken Books, 1965.

9 1/2 x 6 3/8. 222 pp.

9. KAY-KAY COMES HOME. A FABLE OF ENTHUSIASM, by Nicholas Samstag, illustrated by Ben Shahn. New York, Curt Valentin, 1952.

5 7/8 x 9. 44 pp.

10. KUBOYAMA AND THE SAGA OF THE LUCKY DRAGON, by Richard Hudson and Ben Shahn, New York, London, Thomas Yoseloff, 1965.

11 1/4 x 8 3/4. 59 pp. illustrated.

The text by Richard Hudson is based on the book, *The Voyage of the Lucky Dragon,* by Ralph E. Lapp.

11. LOVE AND JOY ABOUT LETTERS, by Ben Shahn. New York, Grossman; Toronto, The Musson Book Co., 1963.

10 1/4 x 13 3/4. 79 pp., in black slipcase.

12. LOVE SONNETS, selected and with notes by Louis Untermeyer, illustrated by Ben Shahn. New York, The Odyssey Press, 1964.

4 1/4 x 6 5/8. 45 pp. illustrated.

13. MAXIMUS OF TYRE, conceived, lettered, and illustrated by Ben Shahn. New York, Spiral Press, 1963.

6 3/4 x 9 1/8. 32 pp. illustrated.

Edition: 50.

14. NOVEMBER TWENTY SIX NINETEEN HUNDRED SIXTY THREE, poem by Wendell Berry, drawings by Ben Shahn. New York, George Braziller, 1964.

7 1/4 x 9 1/4. 32 pp., in black slipcase.

15. OUNCE DICE TRICE, by Alastair Reid, drawings by Ben Shahn. Boston, Toronto, Little, Brown & Co., 1958.

10 1/4 x 7 3/4. 57 pp.

*"An odd collection of words and names to amuze and amaze . . ."*

16. PARAGRAPHS ON ART, by Ben Shahn. New York, Spiral Press, 1952.

    12 pp. illustrated.

    Edition: 1700.

    *"This is the second in a series of brief personal credos prepared at the request of The Spiral Press."*

17. THE SHAPE OF CONTENT, by Ben Shahn. Cambridge, Harvard University Press, 1957.

    9 1/4 x 6 3/8. 131 pp. illustrated.

18. THE SORROWS OF PRIAPUS, by Edward Dahlberg, with drawings by Ben Shahn. Norfolk, Connecticut, New Directions Books, 1957.

    10 3/4 x 7 1/4. 118 pp., in brown slipcase.

    Edition: 150 copies on mould-made Arches paper, signed by the author and the artist; and a trade edition.

19. SWEET WAS THE SONG, musical score and calligraphy by Ben Shahn. New York, Museum of Modern Art, 1956.

    3 1/8 x 5. 28 pp. illustrated.

20. THIRTEEN POEMS, by Wilfred Owen, Northampton, Massachusetts, Gehenna Press, 1956.

    13 1/2 x 10. 35 pp. illustrated with drawings by Ben Shahn, in gray slipcase.

    The portrait of Owen was wood-engraved by Leonard Baskin from a drawing by Shahn, and printed from the wood block.

*ADDENDUM:*

    ECCLESIASTES, handwritten and illustrated by Ben Shahn. Paris, Trianon Press, 1967.

    13 1/8 x 10, green morocco binding, in slip case, illustrated with two original lithographed drawings in red; other plates are reproduced by lithography, collotype, and hand-stencilling.

    Edition: 26 copies, numbered A-Z on Arches Grand Vélin, containing two original lithographed drawings signed by the artist, with an extra set of illustrations, and a progressive series of states of the plates. 200 copies, numbered 1-200 on Arches Vergé, containing one original lithographed drawing signed by the artist. 14 copies are *hors commerce.*

147

# A Partial List of Posters

Ballets. U.S.A. 1959. 31 1/2 x 21 1/4

Boston Arts Festival. Public Garden. 44 x 28

C.I.O. Political Action Committee

From Workers to Farmers . . . THANKS. 39 3/4 x 30

Here there is no poll tax. Register. Vote. 43 1/2 x 27 3/4

Register. The ballot is a power in your hands. 39 3/4 x 30

To Give them a Break. Register. 40 x 29 3/4

For full employment after the war. REGISTER. VOTE. 1944. 30 x 39 1/2

Break Reaction's Grip. 1946. 42 x 30 1/2

WARNING! Inflation Means Depression. Register. Vote. 1946. 42 x 28 1/2

For all these rights we've just begun to fight. 1946. 29 x 38 1/2

WE WANT PEACE. REGISTER. VOTE. 1946. 41 1/2 x 27

Downtown Gallery

Ben Shahn [reproduction of *Triple Dip*]. 28 1/2 x 27 1/2

Fogg Art Museum. Ben Shahn Exhibition ( self-portrait with palette ). 11 x 9

Freda Miller Memorial Concert. 18 1/2 x 12 1/2

Committee for Sane Nuclear Policy

Stop Bomb Tests. 1960. 34 x 44

Lenox Hill Hospital and Skowhegan School of Painting and Sculpture. 1963. 22 x 14

Lincoln Center for the Performing Arts. 1962. 46 x 30

Martha Graham. 30 x 20

National Citizens Political Action Committee
   Our Friend [F. D. Roosevelt] 30 x 39 1/2

Progressive Party
   A Good Man is Hard to Find.
   [Dewey, with Truman at Piano]. 43 3/4 x 29 3/4

Resettlement Administration
   Years of Dust, Rescue Victims, Restore Land to Proper Use. 1936.
   38 x 25

Sheridan Square Playhouse
   Arthur Miller's "A View from the Bridge." 24 x 14

Spoleto
   Festival dei due Mondi. Festival of Two Worlds. 1965. 39 x 27 1/2

U. S. Office of War Information
   This is Nazi Brutality. 1942. 37 3/4 x 28 1/4

United Textile Workers of America
   Organize. We demand the National Textile Act . . . 41 x 27 1/2

War Production Drive Headquarters
   We French Workers Warn You . . . defeat means slavery, starvation,
   death . . . 1942. 28 1/4 x 39 3/4

# Index of Print Titles

*( numbers refer to catalogue entries )*

"O Lord our Father, our young patriots, idols of our hearts, go forth to battle — be Thou near them! With them, in spirit, we also go forth from the sweet peace of our beloved firesides to smite the foe. O Lord our God, help us to tear their soldiers to bloody shreds with our shells; help us to cover their smiling fields with the pale forms of their patriot dead; help us to drown the thunder of the guns with the shrieks of their wounded, writhing in pain; help us to lay waste their humble homes with a hurricane of fire; help us to wring the hearts of their unoffending widows with unavailing grief; help us to turn them out roofless with their little children to wander unfriended the wastes of their desolated land in rags and hunger and thirst, sports of the sun flames of summer and the icy winds of winter, broken in spirit, worn with travail, imploring Thee for the refuge of the grave and denied it — for our sakes who adore Thee, Lord, blast their hopes, blight their lives, protract their bitter pilgrimage, make heavy their steps, water their way with their tears, stain the white snow with the blood of their wounded feet! We ask it, in the spirit of love, of Him Who is the Source of Love, and Who is the ever-faithful refuge and friend of all that are sore beset and seek His aid with humble and contrite hearts.

*A M E N.*"

FROM "THE WAR PRAYER" BY MARK TWAIN

*Giveaway Broadside*

PRINTED AT NORTHLAND PRESS, FLAGSTAFF, ARIZONA

DESIGNED BY JOHN ANDERSON